"*Your last assistant,*" *Shaunna ventured*

"Why did she leave?"

Max stiffened, and the green eyes became cold. Shrugging his shoulders, he said, "For—personal reasons."

"Oh? And what were they?"

He paused for a second. "I'm afraid it was the old story—she fell in love with her boss. That by itself isn't a sacking offense, but I'm afraid she let it affect her work."

Shaunna gave a prim smile. "Well, don't worry, Mr. Ryder—I can assure you I will not fall into the same trap."

"Good, he said abruptly, "I'm very glad to hear it."

But Shaunna thought he didn't sound one little bit convinced!

SHARON KENDRICK was born in West London. Leaving school at sixteen to try a variety of jobs and see the world, she then trained as a nurse. In the best romantic tradition, she fell in love with and married a doctor. While expecting her second child, Sharon got down to writing romantic novels. She loves writing, and the fact that such enjoyable work fits in so well with her life.

No Escaping Love is Sharon's first book.

SHARON KENDRICK

No Escaping Love

Harlequin Books

TORONTO • NEW YORK • LONDON
AMSTERDAM • PARIS • SYDNEY • HAMBURG
STOCKHOLM • ATHENS • TOKYO • MILAN
MADRID • WARSAW • BUDAPEST • AUCKLAND

ISBN 0-373-18606-1

NO ESCAPING LOVE

Copyright © 1993 by Sharon Kendrick.

First North American Publication 1995.

CHAPTER ONE

S<small>HE</small> might just—*just*—make it.

Shauna flung her suitcase and holdall into the empty compartment, clambered in and slammed the door shut just as the train began to move away.

She'd made it with seconds to spare, but, glancing at her watch with a grimace, Shauna realised that, although this might be the express train from Dover to London, it would need to sprout wings and fly if it were going to get her to her interview on time.

She looked out of the window and cursed the stormy skies which had made her ferry crossing so turbulent, before pulling the now crumpled advert out of her holdall. Oh, please—if anyone up there is looking down on me—let me get this job, she thought, as she read it for the umpteenth time.

WANTED

Assistant to businessman in Central London. Hours erratic. Salary excellent. Accommodation available. Initiative and enthusiasm a plus— along with conventional office skills. Languages essential, including *fluent* Portuguese.
Apply in writing to Box No.4204

She had applied, and had received a type-written reply, requesting that she attend for interview at Ryder Enterprises at sixteen-hundred hours today.

The letter had been signed 'Max Ryder' in a firm and rather flamboyant signature.

Some luck, she thought ruefully. It sounded a peach of a job—and she was going to be late.

Exactly three hours later Shauna arrived at Ryder Enterprises, feeling as if she'd been run over by a steamroller. Two years of working in the relatively laid-back atmosphere of Portugal had left her ill-equipped to cope with the frantic bustle of the London Underground.

Struggling with her baggage, she pushed open the heavy glass door and sank into an opulently deep-pile cream carpet. A waft of cloying perfume hit her like a solid wall and her heart sank as she saw the other women in the room. She was in the wrong place! She must be. There was no way that she had *anything* in common with the other occupants of the room. She stood out like a sore thumb.

The three females sitting around a glass table the size of an ice-rink who had been laconically chatting with each other all froze in unison as they looked her up and down. Their assessment lasted less than five seconds before they gave a group demonstration of superior dismissal, then renewed their conversation, ignoring her completely.

Shauna stood stock-still, frozen with indecision, momentarily debating whether or not she should simply turn right round and leave, when she heard a polite cough, and stared across the room into a pair of smiling eyes. The smiling person wore spectacles, had a slick, dark bob and was seated behind a desk. She was speaking now, and it took a couple of seconds for Shauna to realise that she was addressing her.

'I'm Mrs Neilson,' she said. 'And you must be...?'

'Shauna,' she said clearly. 'Shauna Wilde. I'm so sorry,' she walked forward and put her case down by the desk, 'but I'm late.'

Mrs Neilson looked down at a list of names before her. 'Yes, you are,' she agreed. 'And by over an hour, too.' She looked up, her eyes apologetic. 'I'm very sorry, but I'm afraid that Mr Ryder won't tolerate unpunctuality.'

'Oh, but he must!' said Shauna hastily. 'Please?' She smiled at the receptionist, a pleading look in her eye. She had a lot riding on getting this job. 'I've come straight from the Continent—all the way from Portugal. I was making brilliant time but then my ferry was delayed. Can't I just wait until he's interviewed the others? He might see me then.'

'He *might*,' said Mrs Neilson doubtfully, then gave a small smile. 'You can try. Take a seat—but I can't promise anything.'

'Thanks.' Shauna walked over to a chair, dropped her belongings defiantly on the ground beside her and sat down. The eyes all turned in her direction. Well, she decided—this is a game that more than one can play, and she began to stare back.

The more she saw, the more uneasy she became. The three women looked so much *older* than her, and confident. And assured. Very assured. Apart from one elegant creature with short hair—and that must have been cut by someone with a degree in technical drawing, judging by the precision and angles of the style—they had the kind of untamed lion's mane of hair which every woman knew took at least an hour in front of the mirror to achieve. Tousled, yet perfect—while Shauna's was scraped back like a schoolgirl's.

Shauna's hair was undoubtedly her best feature, but black curls which tumbled waistwards were hardly practical for everyday wear. Maybe she should have had it cut to a more manageable length, but she had long since given up going to a hairdresser's for just that purpose. Every hairdresser she'd ever met had managed to talk her out of it.

Shauna looked at the women again. Oh, *why* hadn't she bothered to put some make-up on? Because you slept on the boat and it would have smudged, spoke the voice of reason—and a tiny loo on the train was hardly the place to accurately apply your mascara!

As she waited she considered furtively scrabbling around in her holdall and going off to try and camouflage her shiny face, when a final despairing look at the group convinced her that she would stand no chance against them. They were band-box neat and perfectly co-ordinated. As sleek as well-groomed pedigree cats with their up-market clothes, and Shauna felt like a moggy who'd been left out in the rain all night.

Had things in England really changed that much? she wondered. Was this kind of high-powered dressing really *de rigueur* for a job as a businessman's assistant? Nervously, Shauna tugged at the cuff of her suit.

A door behind the woman at the desk opened, and a blonde sashayed her way out of the room without a word.

Mrs Neilson looked up. 'Would Miss Stevens like to go in next?'

The woman with the short hair headed for the inner sanctum, and Shauna dived into the bottom of her holdall, seriously worried now. Was the job all she had supposed it to be? Had she missed something? Been more naïve than usual? Did these women really look like your run-of-the-mill PAs? Suppose the advertisement was a cover for something else—what had she thought about it sounding too good to be true?

She located the letter nestling against a railway timetable and the remains of an apple-core and read it again. Twice.

No. If there was some subtle message in it then she, Shauna, was too dense to fathom it out. And let's face it, she thought, if you go in there and some guy offers you a job in his massage parlour, then you smile politely and head for the door.

Shauna's fingers, when they replaced the advert, were trembling. She had read about places like this in the Sunday papers. Her imagination began to run away with her. What if they wouldn't let her out? What if a strong hand were to snap itself over her wrist with steely strength...? Don't be so ridiculous, reprimanded an inner voice. Everyone else is getting out, aren't they?

The last woman—a luscious-looking strawberry blonde—went in and the phone on Mrs Neilson's desk bleeped. She picked it up and listened.

'Yes, Mr Ryder—she *is* the last, but Miss Wilde has turned up.' There was a pause. 'Yes, I know she's late, but apparently she's travelled a long way to get here...'

Shauna could hear an angry-sounding voice at the other end of the phone.

'I realise that,' interjected Mrs Neilson. Another pause, while she listened to the voice. 'In my opinion—yes.' She replaced the receiver and looked at Shauna. 'He says he'll see you after the last applicant.' She stood up. 'I must go—I've got a hungry husband at home, champing at the bit,' she grinned. 'Mr Ryder will escort you down to the entrance when the interview's over.' Her voice dropped to a whisper. 'Good luck.'

'Thanks.' Shauna watched her retreat out of the glass door and began to twist at the black corkscrew curl by her ear, a habit which she'd had since childhood, and one which invariably made her look about sixteen, instead of twenty-three.

She must be crazy! She'd be alone in this building with this man Max Ryder—someone she didn't know from Adam! Get out now, the voice urged her. Out of this office, into the lift—press for ground floor, and you're away. She picked up her holdall, and her heart sank to see the strawberry blonde striding out, her eyes glittering, her face a mask of fury.

'Bastard,' she muttered, scarcely audibly, and tottered out of the room on high heels like stilts.

Shauna, now seriously alarmed, sprang to her feet and began walking after her, when a deep voice stopped her in her tracks.

'Going somewhere, Miss Wilde?'

Her heart in her mouth, she turned round reluctantly. 'I don't think I'm suited for the job,' she blurted out, and then her mouth stayed open. She had been conjuring up an image of a small, squat man, with olive skin—possibly with a patch over one eye—and stubby, fat fingers covered with a tasteless display of ostentatious gold rings, but the deep-voiced Mr Ryder couldn't have been more different.

Initially, because he was wearing a suit, she decided that he looked respectable, but closer inspection convinced her that respectable was not the right description at all. Respectable men weren't *that* good-looking!

Every cliché in the book could have been used about this man. Intense. World-weary. Brooding. She'd often read about eyes being like chips of ice and had wondered what that meant. Now she knew. The narrow green eyes which were studying her so closely were as cold as glass. His skin was lightly tanned and his mouth was set in an uncompromising line. She tried to imagine him laughing, and failed.

He was tall. I mean—*I'm* tall, she thought. But this man made her feel like some tiny little thing, which was an entirely new experience for Shauna. He had dark, dark hair with just a bit of a wave in it—a wayward lock curled darkly on the collar of a shirt which even she could tell was silk. The tie was silk too—a pale grey affair which toned perfectly with the darker grey of his suit, a suit which fitted superbly, falling in folds from the broad shoulders, folds which hinted at hard muscle and sinew . . .

'I beg your pardon?' he was saying.

Shauna's grey eyes were like terrified saucers. 'I don't think I'm suited for the job,' she repeated. 'I'm sorry if I've wasted your time.' And proceeded to stare open-mouthed at him again, like a terrified young kitten who had just chanced upon a jungle cat.

'Do please stop gaping at me like an idiot,' he said impatiently. 'And how on earth do you know you're not suited for the job, when you don't know what the job entails? Unless you do know what the job entails, in which case you must be clairvoyant.'

Recognising the heavy sarcasm, she shut her mouth hastily and gave him what she thought was a sweet smile. Humour him, she thought.

He began to look worried. 'You're not about to be ill, are you, Miss Wilde?'

She shook her head. So much for charm! 'I feel fine,' she lied.

'Good,' he said curtly. 'Then, as you've been so good as to give me your time, and I——' here he broke off to glance at a discreet pale gold watch on a tanned wrist '—have set aside mine—then perhaps we could conduct the interview on more formal lines?'

She gulped. 'Sure.' She hooked the holdall over one slim shoulder and picked up her suitcase.

He gestured with his arm. 'After you?' he suggested.

Knowing at once how poor Androcles must have felt as he walked into the lion's den, Shauna stepped unwillingly into the inner sanctum and her eyes lit up.

'Oh, but—it's beautiful!' she exclaimed, as she slowly took in her surroundings.

There was a huge window which took up almost a complete wall, filling the room with a bright, clear light. London lay mapped out before them like a painting. Then other details of the office began to register—the black ash table, a tiny oak bonsai tree and a sheaf of neat papers its only adornment. And the thickness of the pale coffee-coloured carpet in this room made the deep pile of the one in the outer office seem positively threadbare. She'd never seen such an obvious display of wealth, and her earlier misgivings returned to assail her.

'The view I mean,' she finished tamely. 'The view is beautiful.'

The green eyes narrowed. 'I like it,' he said gruffly. He indicated a chair with a wave of his hand, obviously expecting her to sit down, but she remained standing.

'Just a minute,' she blurted out. 'I want you to know that I would never consider doing any-thing—illegal.'

Dark brows shot up. 'Illegal?' His voice was in-credulous. 'Would you care to elucidate?'

She felt on slightly shaky ground, but it was too late to back off now. Assert yourself, some inner voice urged her. Don't let yourself be intimidated by your surroundings. 'I'm afraid that I'm just not interested in escort work,' she managed. 'Or—massage.'

'Massage?' he enquired faintly. '*Massage*? Pray tell me, Miss Wilde—has the front of my building changed dramatically within the last few hours? Am I the victim of a practical joke? Is there now some lurid neon flashing "Girls! Girls! Girls!" outside?'

'No, of course not.'

'Then why on earth should you think that I'd be running some kind of cheap racket like that?' The green eyes glinted ominously.

'Because—because of the other applicants,' she burst out. 'They just didn't look like the type of women who'd be applying for secretarial jobs.'

'Perhaps you could be a little more specific— what exactly was wrong with them?'

She squirmed a little under his scrutiny. 'They looked far too glamorous for that kind of work.'

His mouth turned down at the corners. 'Not glamorous, Miss Wilde. I don't consider glamour to be the over-application of perfume, coupled with a wholly inappropriate use of make-up. Tacky is the adjective which springs to mind. Whereas you . . .'

She didn't know what description he might have considered suitable for her, because he broke off in mid-sentence to study her even more closely than he had done before.

She was glad that the Mediterranean sun had tanned her skin—at least it camouflaged the slight rise in colour which his perusal brought to her cheeks. She knew that she looked clean, and fairly neat, but that was about all that could be said. The black ringlety curls which fell almost to her waist had been pulled back into a french plait, the neatest way of wearing it, but already another corkscrew-like strand had escaped and kept streaking across her face in a dizzy spiral. Her face was completely free of make-up. The legacy of her background had given her naturally long black lashes which fringed the unusual grey eyes.

She wore a navy linen suit, plain and simple. Perhaps not the *best* colour choice for her, but eminently the most practical. Unfortunately she had had it for several years, so the skirt was the wrong length—it brushed to just below her knee instead of this season's style which was several inches above. Her navy leather shoes were completely flat—when you were as tall as she was you *didn't* wear heels!

She met his eyes mutinously, her chin lifting fractionally, peeved at such a leisurely appraisal.

His next words, however, were completely unexpected. '*Gostaria de se sentar, agora?*'

'*Obrigada,*' she said automatically, pulling out a chair from one side of the desk and sitting down, her legs tucked neatly together.

His eyebrows shot up somewhere into the dark hair, as he walked round to the other side of the desk and sat facing her. 'I don't believe it!' he exclaimed. 'You actually speak Portuguese?'

'Of course I do—the advert specified it.'

'It may have specified it, Miss Wilde—but I've been interviewing for three days now, and you're only the second person who has understood and responded to the simplest statement in that language.'

Shauna's eyes widened. 'You mean none of the others today...?'

The tone of his voice bordered on contemptuousness. 'There's one thing, and one thing only, that the assorted bunch I saw today had in common, and that was their avid interest in that ridiculous article—as opposed to the job I'm offering.'

'What article?' asked Shauna in bewilderment. 'I'm not with you.'

The green eyes viewed her with suspicion. 'Then you must be the only woman in the country who hasn't read it.'

'But I haven't *been* in the country,' she pointed out.

He mentioned the name of a well-known women's magazine. 'They decided to do a piece on the fifty most eligible men in Britain,' he growled. 'And since then, it has caused nearly every female coming into contact with me to display even more of the ripe-plum syndrome than usual.'

Shauna had had enough. True, she hadn't exactly warmed to any of her fellow interviewees, but his words were a slur on women in general. She began to rise from her seat. 'What a disgustingly arrogant thing to say——'

'Oh, do sit down, Miss Wilde—you're not in the running for an Oscar, you know. You object to the truth, do you—however unpalatable?'

'I object to your colossal ego,' she said primly. This rejoinder actually brought a wry half-smile to his lips, the first since the 'interview' had commenced, and Shauna was taken aback—his whole face had softened for a moment. The thawing of the glacial green eyes was a definite improvement, she decided.

'My ego may be colossal,' he stated. 'But facts are facts. I'm rich and I'm powerful, and I've known enough women to recognise a blatant invitation when I see it,' he told her arrogantly.

I'll bet you have, she thought fiercely. This man was so big-headed that she was surprised he could walk through the door! 'Well, you needn't fear any "blatant invitation" from me,' she said crossly.

He leaned right back in his chair, his head resting in the palm of his hands, with the careless grace of some jungle feline just before it pounced. 'In that case, Miss Wilde—you could be just what I'm looking for.'

She sat upright in the soft leather chair, meeting the bright green gaze with a candid stare of her own. 'Just what *are* you looking for, Mr Ryder? Your advertisement didn't make it very clear, I must say.'

The green eyes had narrowed to alarming slits. 'Oh, must you? And how would *you* have worded it?'

'I would have thought it was fairly obvious—if you wanted only fluent Portuguese speakers, then the advert should have been written in Portuguese.'

There was a pause. The look he gave her was very measured. She half thought that she saw the merest hint of humour twitch at the corner of his mouth, but then decided that it must have been a trick of the light.

'You are, of course, absolutely right, Miss Wilde. If only the young woman from the specialist staffing agency who came here to take "details" of what I required had been credited with your common sense.'

She ignored his sardonic tone. 'Didn't you tell her what you wanted?'

'Of course I told her!' he barked back. 'But she wasn't listening. She spent the whole time wittering on about "what a beautiful house you have, Mr Ryder" and "your photograph didn't do you justice at *all*, Mr Ryder",' he mimicked.

Shauna gave an almost imperceptible click of disapproval. How *could* she have done? she wondered. Women like that gave women in business a bad name. Quite apart from the fact that you wouldn't need a degree in psychology to recognise that a man like Max Ryder would be completely turned off by such an obvious approach. A man like him would have women in their hundreds, if not *thousands* running after him.

He was still looking at her. 'Am I to understand that you don't approve of women using sex appeal at work?'

Her grey eyes were cold. 'Certainly not. I hope you complained to the agency?'

He shrugged broad shoulders. 'I just shan't use them again. Let's hope I don't have to.' He stared at her consideringly. 'You seem very interested in this staffing agency, Miss Wilde—perhaps you have an affinity for that kind of work?'

'But I'm being interviewed for *this* job, Mr Ryder,' she answered sweetly. She knew that ploy of old. People in power wanted nothing less than one hundred per cent commitment—give them any indication that some other job might suit you more, and you'd be out on your ear. And besides, this job offered her a roof over her head. 'Would you like to tell me a little about it?'

A spark of humour glimmered in the green eyes. 'How about "Tyrant requires PA. Hours long, pay lousy"?' He began to chuckle quietly.

'And is that the truth?' Shauna asked.

A tanned hand moved forward to tap a pencil on the surface of the black ash desk. 'No, I lied about the pay—that's good! The tyrant bit you'd have to make up your own mind about—but I don't suffer fools gladly. I've been called some rather unflattering names in my time,' he said softly. He leaned over to push the bonsai tree a fraction to the right, and then, as if satisfied, settled back in his chair again.

'I buy and sell,' he explained. 'And I deal mainly in property. Since the market has flattened out in this country I've diversified a little, and I'm doing several deals in Europe. At the moment I'm in the process of buying a plot of land in the Algarve which I intend turning into a golf and holiday complex. The project is estimated to take two years minimum, hence the need for an assistant who can speak Portuguese.'

'But you speak it yourself!' she protested.

He shook his head. 'Enough to get by—and I'm very good at ordering in restaurants—but the subtle nuances of the language all go over my head, and I need to understand what is being said. I certainly can't get to grips with legal jargon. Which reminds me—just how good *is* your Portuguese?'

She needed no second bidding. This bit was easy. She wanted to make it clear to him that she, at least, was *not* here on false pretences. That unlike the others she was—as she had stated in her application—perfectly fluent in Portuguese. She spoke rapidly, deliberately making her speech both formal and colloquial—impossible for anyone but the seasoned linguist to understand. When she had finished, she saw that another wry smile had appeared. 'How much did you understand?' she queried.

'Very little,' he admitted. 'You speak very quickly, and your pronunciation is superb.'

She inclined her head, relishing what she accurately assessed was a rare compliment. 'Thank you.'

The eyes were curious. 'How come?'

'How come what?'

'That you're so fluent?'

She hesitated just a little. 'Well,' she said lightly. 'I *have* just spent two years working as a PA in Portugal.'

He waved his hand in the air dismissively. 'I know that. But you must have been pretty good before that? You wouldn't speak it as well as that after just two years.'

He was probing, and she resented it. She didn't want to have to give him a potted history of her life, see pity cloud those enigmatic eyes. She indicated the papers which lay on the desk before him. 'As you'll see from my résumé—I studied languages.' Her grey eyes instinctively flashed a warning.

There was an answering flash in the dark emerald depths. 'To which the same argument applies.'

He was not, she decided, the kind of man to be put off. He was the kind of man who would take a prize for getting blood from a stone. She made up her mind to give him the barest facts possible. 'My mother—was Portuguese,' she stated baldly.

'And your father?'

'Irish.' A flat statement, which dared him to pursue the subject further.

'Unusual combination,' he remarked.

'So I've been told.' She cleared her throat. 'So what you need primarily, Mr Ryder—is an interpreter?'

If he'd noticed that she'd neatly steered the subject away from her parents, he didn't show it. 'Mainly,' he replied. 'But as well as shorthand and typing, I need someone to be my right-hand man, so to speak.' He smiled briefly. 'Or woman, I should say. Someone who will know exactly what I know, and will therefore know how to deal with any urgent business should I not be available. I employ a great many staff not only in this country, but all over the world. Every time some trifling little problem arises, I don't personally want to have to deal with it.' The green eyes held her directly in their full, magnificent gaze.

'I need cables sent,' he continued. 'Documents translated, airline tickets booked, business associates met at the airport. I may need you to travel abroad with me.'

'That sounds like very long hours,' she observed.

'Absolutely. But in return you will be paid hand-somely. You'll have first-class accommodation in London, if you want it, and extremely generous holidays. So what do you think?'

'And how much is the salary?'

The sum he mentioned almost made her fall out of her chair.

'Will you be needing accommodation?' He looked at her quizzically.

'Yes, I will,' she nodded. 'Could you tell me what that consists of?'

There was a moment's hesitation. 'There's a large penthouse flat at the top of this building—part of that will be yours.'

It took her precisely ten seconds to mull it over. He would have to be the worst tyrant ever created to justify her turning a deal like this down. Yes, he seemed a big-head of the worst order, and he himself had admitted that he'd been called some 'unflattering names' in his time. She could think of a few herself! She stared into those unusual green eyes. Surely he couldn't be *that* bad?

And the job—the job was everything she wanted. A secure base, with money to save until she decided what she really wanted to do with her life. But then again, he hadn't offered it to her, had he? No doubt it would be the old, old story of 'I've several other people to see'.

'It sounds very—adequate,' she said cautiously.

This last remark inspired a throaty laugh. 'Adequate? What a ghastly word! Miss Wilde, if you're going to work for me you must promise me faithfully that you will never use the word "adequate" ever again.'

She let the flippancy go. 'You mean—you're—you're offering . . . ?'

His face was quite serious again. He gestured to the sheaf of papers on his desk. 'I've seen your references, which are excellent—though you, Miss Wilde, would probably have said "adequate". You satisfy all my other criteria—your Portuguese is fluent, you seem bright enough—oh, and you don't fall into the man-eating tigress mould.'

Meaning, thought Shauna acidly, that I'm a plain Jane.

'And one other thing,' his voice was lower now. 'You need this job, don't you?'

Yes, she needed the job, but she wasn't desperate. She knew that nothing was a bigger turn-off than desperation. 'There are other jobs,' she said coolly.

He smiled. 'The job's yours if you want it.'

She had actually been reaching for her holdall, when she stared at him, not believing her ears. 'Pardon?'

'The job's yours,' he repeated. 'If you want it.'

She still didn't believe it. 'Just like that?' she asked cautiously.

'Just like that.'

She pretended to hesitate, but she got the impression that he wasn't fooled for a minute.

'In that case,' she said, resisting the temptation to leap up into the air, 'I'd be happy to accept.'

'Good.'

'When would you like me to start?'

He frowned. 'Is tomorrow too soon?'

She wanted to make amends for her earlier flights of fancy. 'Tomorrow's fine.'

A piercing look came into his eyes. 'Today, you were late,' he accused.

'There was a . . .' she began, but he held his hand up.

'I'm not interested. I'm prepared to overlook it once—it won't happen again.'

'No,' she said quietly—she wouldn't dare!

He closed his eyes briefly for a moment, and yawned. She noticed how intensely weary he looked, and wondered whether that was work, or play. When he opened them again, he found Shauna staring at him intently.

He blinked. 'What is it?'

'Your last assistant,' she ventured. 'Why did she leave?'

He stiffened, and the green eyes became cold again. Shrugging his shoulders, he said, 'For—personal reasons.'

Repressing hysterical thoughts, she forced her voice to sound casual. 'Oh? And what were they?'

He paused for a second. 'I'm afraid it was the old story—she fell in love with her boss. That by itself isn't a sackable offence, but I'm afraid she let it affect her work.'

There was no mistaking the warning in his voice. Don't make the same mistake, it seemed to say.

Resisting an urge to comment on the girl's mental state at the time, for surely she must have been loopy to fall for such an insufferably arrogant man, Shauna gave a prim smile. 'Well, don't worry, Mr

Ryder—I can assure you that I will not fall into the same trap.'

'Good,' he said abruptly. 'I'm very glad to hear it.'

But Shauna thought he didn't sound one little bit convinced.

CHAPTER TWO

MAX RYDER'S next words were, however, brisk and businesslike. 'I assume that you've clothes and stuff to collect?' He looked down at Shauna's rather battered suitcase. 'Or do I take it that's the sum total of your worldly goods?' he asked sarcastically.

'No, you do not!' she retorted indignantly, pushing away a dark curl which was tickling the corner of her mouth. 'Don't forget—I *have* just come off the boat. As a matter of fact—I've got two more suitcases.'

'So where have you left them?'

'They've been in store at some friends' flat.'

The green eyes beneath the dark brows were looking at her questioningly. 'Local?'

'Yes,' she nodded. 'In London.'

He gave a heavy sigh. 'Are you being deliberately obtuse, Miss Wilde?' He glanced at the pale gold watch. 'I'm expecting a call from Paris at eight—I can give you a lift to collect your belongings, then when we get back I'll show you over the flat.'

She shook her head, so that two more curls wiggled out. For some reason, she was reluctant to be driven there by this man. He was her boss, and—she had to admit—dangerously attractive. She didn't want contact with him spilling over into her private life. 'That's very kind of you, but I can manage on my own, honestly.'

'Oh, for God's sake!' he exclaimed impatiently. 'I'm not trying to unlock the secrets of your soul— I'm simply offering you a lift. Why struggle on the Tube when you can do it in comfort? And if you're worried about some boyfriend—ex or otherwise— rushing out to hit me on the jaw, then don't. Like the proverbial wise man—I'll hear, see nor speak evil!'

The very idea was laughable. She simply couldn't imagine anyone having the temerity to hit *this* man on the jaw! Quite apart from anything else it looked as though it were fashioned from granite.

'I happened to share with two lawyers, not cavemen,' she retorted. 'And they live in Hampstead.'

To her surprise, the questioning ceased. 'Hampstead's miles away,' he said briefly. 'It would take you all night to get there. Come on—we'll take the car.'

She followed him in silence out of the office and into the lift. At the ground floor he introduced her to Charlie, the commissionaire. Then he ushered her through heavy revolving glass doors and outside, where the light was fading rapidly from the sky. The typically October temperature had plummeted rapidly now that the sun had disappeared and Shauna shivered involuntarily, her linen jacket seeming totally inadequate. She hadn't thought he'd been looking, but he noticed immediately.

'I hope there's a thicker coat among your things?' he commented.

'Yes, I've got an overcoat.' She didn't like to say that all her things would probably look to him as if they'd come out of the Ark! Two years was a long time in fashion, and department stores had only recently begun to realise that not all women were of medium height and build. Shauna, being tall and very slim, had always found it notoriously difficult to find clothes to fit her.

Their steps led them to the back of the building, where he unlocked a cunningly concealed car-port to reveal the low, sleek lines of a Mercedes. He was a good driver—confident, but not over-confident. He drove the powerful machine well within the limits of the city's speed restrictions. She thought it rather a waste to have such a powerful car if he lived in town. They headed north.

'So tell me,' he said, 'how on earth you managed to survive two years working in a foreign country on your own.'

'What's that supposed to mean?' she declared indignantly.

He shrugged, the glimmer of a smile playing on his lips. 'If you thought I was running a massage parlour and escort agency, then your imagination must have been working overtime when you were abroad.'

She flushed. Her daydreaming had got her into trouble on more than one occasion. 'I'm surprised you gave me the job.'

A brown hand expertly and swiftly changed down into second gear as a taxi shot out of a side-street and into their path. 'I had a strong gut feeling about you, and I tend to rely on my instincts—where business is concerned, at any rate,' he finished.

She began to wonder how he might respond where his emotions were concerned. If indeed he had any! She remembered his conceited remark about women displaying the 'ripe-plum syndrome'—meaning, presumably, that they all fell eagerly into his arms, she thought acidly. But he'd been nothing but disparaging about her fellow job applicants, so he obviously wasn't desperate for scalps to notch up. She sneaked a surreptitious sideglance at him in the darkness of the car. How old would he be? Early thirties? Involved? Someone as eligible as Max Ryder would be bound to be involved. Except that she couldn't recall seeing any photographs in that vast office of his. Come to think of it, it had been one of the most impersonal rooms that she had ever been in. Stark and dramatic. Even the bonsai tree on the plain black desk had given nothing away. Stunning, but impersonal. A bit like him, really.

'So you managed to spend two years on the Continent without getting yourself into any scrapes?' he probed.

The way he said it made her feel about ten years old. 'I'd been used to working in Portugal,' she defended. 'After two years I knew the job inside out and back to front. I got back to England and suddenly I felt like a stranger in my own country. When I walked into your building I felt totally out of place—it was so outside my experience that I imagined the worst possible scenario.' She tucked one of the errant curls behind her ear and looked at him slightly nervously. 'Do you understand what I mean?'

Unexpectedly he said, 'I believe I do.'

The curl sprang back. 'Can we forget it, and put it down to travel fatigue? By the way—it's left here.'

The car swung up the tree-lined road. The trees were beginning to lose their leaves now. It seemed such a long time since she had lived here—a lifetime ago, really. Nick and Harry had been great flat-mates to have—kind and protective, just like the brothers she'd never had.

'Nice area,' he commented.

'Yes, it is. Could you pull up here? It's the second house, behind the van.'

The powerful car pulled smoothly to a halt. He turned to face her in the semi-darkness. 'I'll wait here,' he said. 'Let me know if you need a hand with anything.'

'Thanks.' She climbed out of the low car, walked to the front door and pressed the bell.

She had to wait several minutes, and was contemplating leaving a note, when the door was opened and a tall, tousled-haired young man stood stock-still, and then a grin split his face in two.

'Shauna!' he said in surprise, and then, 'Shauna!' again in a tone of delight. 'You dark horse, you! Why didn't you say?'

'Because I didn't know until recently,' she laughed. 'And you know the advert you sent me? I got the job!'

'You got the job!' he echoed in delight, and before she could stop him he had caught her up in his arms and whirled her round and round.

'Put me down, Harry,' she giggled. 'You'll give yourself a hernia!' But as he carefully lowered her back on to the step she saw over his shoulder that Max Ryder was no longer sitting in his car, but lounging against the bonnet—his expression in the darkness unreadable, but, even in that outwardly relaxed stance, there was no mistaking the coiled tension in the long limbs. Obviously, he must have seen Harry embrace her, and she wondered why she should mind that he had.

Harry looked at her closely. 'You look fabulous, Shauna,' he said quietly. 'But pensive. Come in. Have a drink?'

She shook her head regretfully, eyeing the familiarly shabby hall with affection. 'I can't. I've got someone waiting. He's offered me a job and accommodation. I'm here to collect my stuff.'

'So? Invite him in, too.'

Shauna took in the overflowing books, the half-empty wine bottle, last Sunday's—and the Sunday's before that!—newspapers littering the floor. She could just imagine the minimalist, bonsai-loving Max Ryder fitting in here!

'I don't think so, Harry,' she smiled at him fondly. 'He hasn't even shown me the flat, yet—and he's expecting a phone call from Paris. But I'll come round another night—you can cook me one of your famous Bolognese sauces, and we'll catch up on all the gossip.'

Harry frowned. 'If only we hadn't let your old room out.'

'I would hardly have expected you to hold on to it for two years!' exclaimed Shauna. 'That would be stretching friendship a little too far!'

'No, I suppose not.'

'It was good of you to keep my stuff for me.' She looked at her watch. 'Listen, I'd better not keep——'

'No, of course not. I'll get your stuff.' He retreated into the larger bedroom. 'Nick will be sorry to have missed you,' he called out. 'Did you know he's in love?'

'He wrote and told me! What's she like?'

He reappeared, carrying two large suitcases. 'Great—when she's not sitting gazing at him like a lovesick puppy!'

'You next, then,' teased Shauna.

'Is that an offer?' he smiled.

They heard a loud toot from outside before she had a chance to reply. Shauna knew immediately who it would be.

'That'll be my new boss,' she explained. 'I'd better go.'

Harry pushed the curtain open a crack. 'Flash car,' he observed. 'What's he like?'

Shauna peeped out—he was *still* standing there. 'The kind of man your mother told you never to go out with—well, *most* mothers,' amended Shauna.

'Lucky devil,' said Harry gloomily. 'I have the opposite trouble—instant parental approval—very boring!'

There was a momentary pause. 'Thanks for my free holiday,' he smiled. 'I had a great time.'

He'd travelled out to Portugal in the summer, and her boss had put him up for the fortnight.

She grinned her agreement. 'Me too. And thanks again for finding me the ad.'

They stood for a moment, hands clasped like the old friends they were—their brief and youthful romance long forgotten. 'I'll carry your cases to the car for you,' he said.

A dark figure loomed up out of the shadows. 'There's no need for that,' contradicted a deep voice, and Shauna started to see Max Ryder standing there, automatically moving away to break the contact, wondering what had caused the faint upward curl of his lip.

She performed the necessary introductions, but she thought that her new boss was decidedly lukewarm in his greeting, and Harry was uncharacteristically taciturn. In fact, for some reason neither man seemed to like the other very much.

Amid promises to call soon, Shauna and Max roared off down the street. There was silence for a moment. Then he spoke.

'I thought I asked you not to be long,' he said tetchily as he put his foot down on the accelerator. 'I hope I'm not going to miss my call.'

'Sorry,' she said automatically.

Max gave her a sideways glance. 'After such a fond reunion, I'm surprised your lover doesn't want you to stay with him.'

So he *had* seen them embrace. 'He is not my lover,' she said, in an angry voice. Not any more, she thought. An attempt at young love years ago which had fizzled out almost as soon as it had started. Not that she was going to explain that to *him*. He was her boss, and he had absolutely no right whatsoever to comment on her private life. 'And even if he were, it's none of your business.' Which didn't come out at all the way she had intended it to.

She saw his hands tighten on the steering-wheel, as if he was not used to being spoken to in such a way, and she might have tried to amend her snapped response, but a glance at the cold, hard profile told her that she would be wise to say nothing, so she stared out into the night as Hyde Park swept by them.

He didn't speak again until they had arrived back in Mayfair. He was not, Shauna decided, the type of man to engage in meaningless pleasantries.

'I'll show you the apartment now.' He frowned as he glanced again at the pale gold wristwatch. 'You must be hungry.'

So he was back to being civil. 'Starving,' she admitted.

This time, the lift went right past the third floor where he'd interviewed her, and the doors opened straight into an enormous sitting-room. The carpet was white, and littered with Persian rugs. The walls were also white, with several large modern canvases which fitted in perfectly with the simple leather furniture.

Shauna suppressed a gasp. Surely he couldn't mean that *this* was her flat? Compared to the dark cubby-hole she'd had in Lisbon, this place was like a palace.

'The kitchen's through here,' he was saying. 'There's a bathroom off that passage over there, but of course your room has its own, *en suite*. This is your room here.' He pushed open a door to reveal a sumptuously appointed bedroom, decorated in palest eau-de-Nil. 'You'll find that—apart from work—we'll hardly see one another.'

Shauna's mouth fell open. 'We? What do you mean "we"?'

He sounded impatient. 'The flat has three bedrooms, and a great deal of living space. We'll hardly be on top of one another.'

Suddenly the tall, dark figure of Max Ryder appeared very slightly menacing, and involuntarily she took a step back. 'But I didn't know I was going to be sharing with *you*!'

'Oh, for God's sake! We are living in the twentieth century, you know!' he retorted. 'Men and women *do* share flats these days—as you've obviously done yourself before. Or perhaps you consider yourself such a little sexpot that you think I won't be able to keep my hands off you?'

'No, I don't!' she parried, a blush creeping into her cheeks as her mind became alight with vivid images that his words had conjured up.

'Well, that's something,' he said, with a kind of grim satisfaction. 'Because, believe me, the last type of woman to attract me is some tall, skinny kid who doesn't look old enough to be out of gymslips!'

Shauna glared at him. It was one thing to decide that the man before her was the last person she'd ever fall for—it was quite another to discover that he felt exactly the same way—and his disparaging remarks made her bristle with indignation. Share a flat with *him*? Why, she'd rather share with a gang of escaped convicts!

'And what about—privacy?' she asked primly.

He gave a hollow laugh. 'Privacy? Will you stop acting like the original vestal virgin? Slightly redundant anyway, since we've just collected your stuff from your ex-lover.'

He managed to make a young love-affair sound so *sordid*, she thought, her grey eyes sending out sparks of indignation.

'You'll have all the privacy you could possibly want,' he continued. 'For a start, I'm away in the country most weekends. Secondly, your room is on the opposite side of a very large flat, and it has its own bathroom. So does mine. So the chances of your coming across me in the raw are pretty remote.' His eyes narrowed. 'The good news for both of us is that I'll shortly be having the flat divided into two completely separate apartments. It would have been done already if *I* had been here to sort the damned builders out. Unfortunately, I've been out of the country.'

That explained the tan, thought Shauna.

His eyes were mocking as they surveyed her. 'Now, are those arrangements secure enough for your Victorian sensibilities, or would you like me to throw in a chastity belt while I'm at it?' He gave an unexpected grin as he saw her colour heighten yet again.

'You know, you really are going to have to do something about that blushing, if you're going to work for me. And you a woman of the world!'

His teasing immediately defused the atmosphere. 'I am *not* a woman of the world, if that means what I think it means.'

He was staring at her curiously. 'Tell me, you didn't lie about your age in your letter, did you?'

'Oh, for goodness' sake!' she flung back at him. 'Of course I didn't lie! Do you always think the worst of people, or are you just used to people lying to you?'

'All the time,' he mused. 'Particularly women, and particularly about their age. Except that they usually lop a few years off, whereas in your case...'

There was something distinctly unsettling about the way those green eyes bored into her, she thought, but, refusing to rise to this, she stared steadily at him. 'Will you be needing me this evening?' she asked pointedly. 'Because I'd like to unpack and——'

He shook his head. 'You're free until tomorrow morning at ten sharp. Oh, and there's one more thing—house rules.'

'I am very tidy,' she interrupted. 'And I do not leave dirty dishes in the sink.'

'There's a dishwasher, actually—and the maid comes in twice a week. No, I've only one rule and that's no overnight guests. I don't care who you go to bed with—just don't do it here. I don't intend to have my sleep disturbed.'

She went white beneath her tan and glared at him. He was obviously going out of his way to shock her, but he was going to be disappointed—she had absolutely no intention of rising to his challenge, *or* of offering him any information on the current state of her love-life. The question was whether she could put up with working for a man who could be quite so contentious. She continued to stare at him as she contemplated the only alternative, which would be to walk out of here right now.

She couldn't. It was a brilliant job—she'd never find another like it. And if the only fly in the ointment was the conceited Max Ryder—well, surely she could put up with that? And at least he had made it perfectly clear that he wouldn't dream of making a pass at her, so in that sense, at least, she was quite safe with him.

The green eyes had been observing her with the faintest touch of amusement. 'Changed your mind, have you?'

She pretended to look perplexed. 'Changed my mind? About what?'

'Staying.'

Her wide mouth closed in a determined line. Roll on the day when the builders arrived! 'Certainly not, Mr Ryder. I look on it as a challenge.'

The glimmer of a smile. 'Call me Max. And there's plenty of food in the kitchen. Help yourself.'

'Thank you very much,' she answered politely, but, as she closed her bedroom door behind her, she reflected that her voracious appetite of earlier had mysteriously disappeared.

CHAPTER THREE

SHAUNA unpacked her cases and her holdall and hung everything up in the vast mirrored wardrobe, deciding wryly that she would really have to invest in some new clothes. What she had was OK, but there was so little of it. In Portugal she'd lived mostly in lightweight clothes which were totally inappropriate for the approaching English winter. At least the stuff she'd picked up at the flat was warmer, but, even so, it now looked terribly dated.

The bathroom looked like something out of an ideal home advertisement—all mirrors and lights and expensive-looking glass-topped bottles. She took a long, luxurious bath, which was heaven after all the travelling, and finished off in the shower, untying the rampant black curls and smothering them with shampoo, then conditioner. It took her almost half an hour to dry them, and by that time she was exhausted and barely had the energy to brush her teeth and climb into the king-sized bed. It had been a long day.

She had thought that she wasn't hungry, but her stomach obviously thought differently since she woke up in the night feeling distinctly empty. She sat up in bed, rubbing her eyes with the back of her fist, her heart sinking when she saw that her watch read only four a.m.—hardly the proper time to eat. Her stomach rumbled loudly in protest.

Perhaps if she was *very* quiet, she could go and raid Max's larder—he'd told her to help herself, after all.

She climbed out of bed and pulled on her robe. Barefooted, she quietly opened the bedroom door and listened for a moment. She could hear nothing other than the faint ticking of a clock somewhere in the distance. Max Ryder's bedroom door was closed, thank goodness. Silently she padded over the thick pile of the carpet, the soft woollen strands tickling her toes. She reached the kitchen and gently opened the door.

Whatever else he might or might not have done, Max Ryder certainly ate well. The fridge was full of salads, cold meats, cheeses, fruit, and an expensive-looking box of Belgian chocolates. Further hunting produced a bread-bin, and she cut herself two enormous slices of brown bread, buttered them, and layered salad and ham between them.

She had just found a full carton of orange juice and was about to open it when she heard a sound behind her and whirled round to find Max Ryder standing at the door, wearing nothing but a pair of faded denims—and only half-zipped, she noted in horror before averting her gaze from them so hastily that the carton of juice slipped from her fingers.

At precisely the same moment, they both lunged for the juice, Shauna's outstretched hand making her lose her balance, her bare feet slipping wildly on the shiny tiles. She would have fallen awkwardly had his arm not reached out automatically and, as she toppled, he caught her.

Winded, she sagged against him, momentarily too dazed to be aware of anything other than his strength as he held her, of the tingling warmth of his hand as it casually spanned her back, and then, as her senses returned, she realised to her horror that she was clasped close to him, that her breasts were jutting firmly against the warm skin of his bare chest—their shape clearly defined through the wool of her robe. A strange wave of dizziness assailed her and colour washed her cheeks as she saw that the way she was leaning against him had caused a bare breast to slip free of the confines of her robe, so that almost the whole of the milky-pale globe— untouched by the hot summer sun—was visible.

She heard him swear beneath his breath and she hastily pulled away, breathing rapidly, unable to meet his eyes for embarrassment as she pulled the gown tightly around herself, as if it were armour-plating. The thick maroon dressing-gown had been chosen with no concessions to fashion, warmth and hard-wearingness being its main function, but all of a sudden she might have been clothed in some feminine little wisp of satin, she felt so exposed under his gaze.

'What the hell are you playing at?' he grated, in a loud, harsh voice, and she noticed a small muscle working on his left cheek. He pushed her out of the way almost roughly, slammed the orange juice down on the work surface, and stood facing her.

'Is this your idea of entertainment?' he demanded. 'Hurling things around the kitchen at this God-forsaken hour? Not to mention yourself!'

'That was an accident—I slipped on the floor. You frightened me,' she protested.

'Frightened you? You're bloody lucky I didn't rugby tackle you to the ground,' he snapped. 'I heard noises, and I thought it was an intruder.'

The remark about the rugby tackle was a little too close for comfort. 'Oh, for goodness' sake! Does this mean that every time I walk around the apartment you're going to start throwing yourself at me like the caped crusader?'

The green eyes were cold. 'As I recall,' he said icily, 'it was you who threw yourself at me.'

'And I told you it was an accident! I am now sharing this flat with you, in case you'd forgotten, and that means that from time to time I will be making some little noise or movement,' she said, sweetly sarcastic.

'It sounded like Nelly the Elephant stomping around,' he retorted. 'And do you always make a habit of eating sandwiches at four in the morning?'

Boss he might be—custodian he was not! 'I eat when I'm hungry—like now! So if you wouldn't mind letting me get on with it...'

'I'm going,' he snapped moodily. 'Just try and make less noise on your return trip, will you? And put the light out.'

As he stomped out of the kitchen, she had to resist a very strong urge indeed to stick her tongue out at him. She waited until she heard his door close quietly, before perching on a stool and shakily pouring herself some juice.

He had implied that he was a tyrant. *Tyrant*? That was the understatement of the century! She could have provided a far more colourful description! He was the foulest-tempered, meanest man she'd ever encountered. She bit into the sandwich viciously. He also had one of the best bodies she'd ever seen—and she'd seen hundreds, bronzed and posing on beaches all over Portugal. There hadn't been a trace of surplus flesh on that frame, even when he bent down. He had also been perfectly at ease with his semi-clothed state, completely unselfconscious, which was more than could be said about her.

She bit into the sandwich again, wishing that she could dispel the sinking wave of disconcertion that washed over her as she recalled the way that her breasts had pressed against him. The way in which her robe had fallen open... She pressed her knuckles to the sides of her head, the sandwich forgotten. What if he'd thought it deliberate? His ego was so immense, his opinion of women so low, that he probably hadn't put it past her to wake him up in the middle of the night, and then to drape herself provocatively all over him, like some amateurish *femme fatale*.

A small groan escaped her. Please don't let him think that, she prayed. After all, hadn't one of his criteria for employing her been that she didn't 'fall into the man-eating tigress mould'?

She finished off the rest of the sandwich and stacked her plate and glass in the dishwasher. As she tiptoed back to bed, she resolved that, unless there was a fire, Max Ryder would never again see her in any form other than fully dressed—that way there could be no misinterpreting her motives!

* * *

Although there wasn't much of the night left, Shauna opted for sleep, and, much to her surprise, it came. When she opened her eyes it was nine-fifteen and bright sunshine was streaming in through a crack in the silk curtains.

Ten o'clock sharp, he had said, so she had to hurry, although, as she towelled herself dry after a brief shower, she decided that it wouldn't come as any great shock to her to learn that he had reconsidered his job offer after the orange juice incident.

She dressed in a simple black tunic, but she relieved its starkness with a scarlet ribbon at the nape of her neck which loosely tied back the thick black curls.

Feeling ready to face the world—or, more importantly, him—she opened her bedroom door, hoping against hope to find the sitting-room empty, but she was out of luck, for he sat there at the table by the window, as large as life, with a coffee-pot steaming in front of him.

He looked up as she entered, and she braced herself for a barrage of abuse, or a cold dismissal, but there was neither—he barely glanced up from his newspaper, except to say, 'The coffee's fresh,' gesturing to the pot before him.

She hesitated for a moment, and eventually he looked up at her, his expression as inscrutable as if it had been carved in marble.

'About last night,' she began.

'Forget it,' came the curt rejoinder.

What was it that made her persist, when his tone expressly forbade it? 'But I . . .'

'I said *forget* it!' The green eyes looked as dark as jade.

'I didn't want you to think——' she began stubbornly. What? That she'd been out to seduce him?

'Listen to me,' he interrupted exasperatedly. 'I thought nothing. Do you understand? *Nothing*. You may have thought it appropriate to act like some damsel in distress—personally I thought your reaction was way over the top.' A cynical smile twisted his lips. 'Cowering in the corner, defending your supposed honour. Believe me, what I saw was less than I'd have seen on any beach anywhere in the world, and certainly nothing to get excited about. So can we please drop it?' He picked up his newspaper summarily. 'Now eat up your toast like a good girl,' he finished sarcastically.

She forced her hand to remain steady as she reached out for the coffee-pot, scarcely crediting what she'd heard, too stung by his cutting put-down to be able to think of a suitable retort. Nothing to get excited about! What a nerve! Of all the high-handed, arrogant swines, she thought as she determinedly ate her way through one slice of toast and began a second—she was not going to let him see how angry his hurtful comments had made her, by being off her food!

No wonder he was paying her such a high salary—danger money, that was what it was! And now here she was, ensconced in the home of this unbelievably rude man. The future certainly did not look very promising.

She pulled one of the newspapers on the table towards her, but couldn't really take much in. She thought what a strange picture they must make, sitting drinking early morning coffee together, when they were virtual strangers. But didn't that happen all the time with flat-sharing? They said you never really learnt what someone was like until you lived with them. What surprised her was that Max Ryder wasn't already living with a woman—in the *full* meaning of the term.

She realised that she knew absolutely nothing about him, other than the obvious...that he was tall, dark and handsome and—according to him, at least!—had a lethal effect on women. When she looked up from the paper, whose words were a mystery to her, her grey eyes all dreamy and miles away, she found him surveying her curiously.

'A woman who doesn't chatter in the morning—now that *is* something I could get used to.'

And here, no doubt, he would be rewarded with gushing thanks, she thought drily. 'Didn't you say you wanted to start work when we'd finished our coffee?' she asked coolly.

Her raised his eyebrows by just a millimetre. 'Why, certainly,' he murmured. 'If we could just convene to the office, I'll give you a list.'

He picked up a green silk tie which he had thrown over the back of the chair. It was almost the exact colour of his eyes and Shauna found herself wondering if he'd chosen it with precisely that in mind!

She followed him out. It felt odd to be travelling down from the flat to the offices just two floors below. A bit like going from a hotel bedroom down to the dining-room, she decided, then bent her head quickly to study an imaginary spot on her black patent shoes. Bedroom! Now, what on earth had made her think of hotel bedrooms? Thank heavens that Max Ryder couldn't read her mind!

Mrs Neilson, the receptionist, was already in place. 'Morning, Max,' she smiled.

'Hi, Rosie. You met yesterday, but may I formally introduce Shauna Wilde, who got the job?'

Rosie Neilson extended a perfectly manicured hand. 'Nice to see you again, Shauna. I knew you'd walk the job, the moment I saw you.'

'How d'you do?' said Shauna politely, slightly alarmed at this. I hope I'm nothing like the last assistant, she thought. The one he had to get rid of!

'We'll be in my office all morning,' said Max. 'Can you hold all non-urgent calls for the first hour?'

'Will do. I'll rescue you with coffee later.'

Shauna and Max went into his office, and, from that moment on, he kept her busy—and how! For the first hour she scribbled furiously in a small notebook while he explained the framework of his day. 'Although, of course—no two days are ever the same,' he said.

He gave her the phone numbers of clients and colleagues, of hotels As far as she could make out, ... to stay in, and res- ... so many fingers in so many pies that he could have done with a couple of extra sets of hands!

After the first hour was up, the phone on his desk began to ring. The first call was from Paris, and he dealt with that himself, speaking in a very passable French accent. Then he set to—dictating a whole heap of letters, and asking her to write one to his Portuguese lawyer.

'These are the main points I want to make—just make it formal, but flowery—you know the kind of thing they like?'

She nodded. 'I do.'

He went out for early lunch—he didn't say who with, she assumed it was business—leaving her to fend for herself in his absence. Surprisingly enough, she coped, even when Mrs Neilson went off at lunchtime.

She typed the letters he'd dictated and he came back just before five and pronounced himself satisfied. She supposed it would have been too much to ask that he actually beam his gratitude; instead she had to make do with a brisk 'Thanks' before he informed her that he was going out for the evening and gave her a spare set of keys to the flat. She mystified and infuriated herself by wondering just who he was out with.

Within a few days she had settled into some sort of routine. She worked hard—he certainly expected it!—perhaps harder than ever before in her life. He was exacting, demanding and critical to the extreme if she fell short of excellence. And yet she found the standards of working for such a hard taskmaster strangely satisfying. She became determined that he should not find her deficient in any of the skills he expected her to have.

Once, she caught him listening to her conducting a conversation entirely in Portuguese, the expression on his face a cross between amusement and irritation. She suspected it peeved him that she was fluent, whereas he was not!

In the flat she saw him less than she would have imagined—he was right, it *was* very big. He went out some evenings, never saying where, never inviting her to go with him, but then, why should he?

Once or twice, she'd answered the phone to a woman with a distinctively low voice called Marta. She was bursting with curiosity to know who she was, but he always took the calls in his bedroom.

Shauna tended to disappear to her room after supper to read, or, if he wasn't around, she'd watch TV or a video. Once, she had dinner with Harry and Nick, and Nick's girlfriend, Heather—but Shauna knew immediately that it wouldn't become a regular thing. Nick was too much in love, and Harry was studying for his Bar exams. Sadly, she recognised that they had all inevitably grown apart since they'd been at university together.

A fortnight went by with Shauna scarcely seeing Max at home, and she made up her mind to try to break the ice a little. After all, they *were* flatmates, and, just because they were also boss and employee, that shouldn't in theory preclude some sort of friendship.

One day—just before he set off for lunch—she casually asked him whether he'd be eating out that evening.

He grimaced. 'God, no—I've had a surfeit of restaurant food this week.'

Perfect! She would cook one of her wholewheat spaghetti dishes as she'd sometimes done with

Harry and Nick, and get to know a little of the person behind the enigmatic façade of her employer. Except that it didn't quite turn out like that...

Max emerged from his room at around eight to find the table set for two and Shauna busy stir-frying vegetables, her face pink and shiny from the heat.

His brow creased suspiciously. 'Having company?' he asked, his tone leaving her in no doubt what he thought of *that* idea.

She smiled. 'Not exactly—that is—I hoped that you might like to join me?'

'*Whaat*?' he queried.

Her smile faded a little. 'I was just rustling up some supper for myself, and, as you weren't going out tonight, I thought...' Her voice died away as she saw his face. If she'd suggested dining on old socks he couldn't have looked more aghast.

He looked at the frying-pan, which contained the snow-peas, baby corn and zucchini, and gave a barely suppressed shudder, before turning the direction of his gaze back to Shauna, the green eyes looking distinctly unfriendly.

'Let's get a couple of things straight, shall we?' he said, in a deliberately neutral voice. 'The way to my heart is not through my stomach—got that?'

She frowned non-comprehendingly. 'I don't——'

'Neither am I,' he continued relentlessly, 'going to be impressed if you start baking cakes your granny taught you to. Similarly, flowers filling the apartment, or the smell of fresh coffee wafting through the air, are less likely to fill me with admiration at your home-making skills, than with boredom.'

The fullness of her mouth became distorted into a straight line as she bit her bottom lip in anger. 'I don't know what you're talking about,' she snapped.

He leaned forward as if to emphasise his point, so close that she could see the dramatic contrast between the bright green of his eyes and the stark jet of their centres. 'Then let me tell you. I am talking about your little "womanly wiles",' he sniped sarcastically. 'Why is it that whenever I'm around women they suddenly show an irresistible desire not only to cook and sew, or to endlessly straighten already straight pictures, but also to coo with delight whenever they spot a baby or a fluffy kitten?' he mused sarcastically. 'Perhaps you could throw some interesting new light on the subject?'

The primary rule of deference to one's superior flew straight out of the window and there was a momentary flash of rage in her grey eyes before she quelled it. No need to let him see how much his conceited rejection had hurt her. She managed a scornful laugh.

'Over-reacting *just* a little, aren't you, Max?' she enquired mockingly. 'I've hardly been out at dawn picking mushrooms to prepare a lavish banquet. It was a simple supper that I thought you might like to share—if I'd known it was going to cause *quite* so much fuss, then I wouldn't have bothered. I shan't again.'

'Good,' he said curtly. 'I am sick of women deciding that I am to be the lucky recipient of their search for a permanent partner. I am *not* looking for love. Understand? And now I'm going out.'

Speechless with indignation, she watched as he walked to the door, the electric light gleaming on the dark, tangled waves of his hair, watching his every stride, every damned muscular move of him, and it wasn't until he had slammed the front door that she allowed herself the luxury of a very loud and very graphic expletive.

A fortnight later, Max was dictating another letter for her to type and standing in front of the enormous plate-glass window which dominated the office, when the phone on the desk began to ring and Shauna reached out to pick it up.

'Mr Ryder's office,' she announced briskly.

'Is Mr Ryder there?' asked an efficient-sounding female voice.

'Who's calling, please?'

'This is Queen Mary's School.'

Max was looking at her enquiringly.

'It's Queen Mary's School,' she said, pressing the mute button on the phone.

He took the receiver at once, looking slightly puzzled as he did so. 'Hello?'

She couldn't help noticing that his expression changed from puzzlement to something fast approaching anger, or that his barked monosyllabic questions had become increasingly terse.

He gave a curt goodbye and replaced the receiver noisily as he got to his feet. 'I have to go out now, Shauna. I may be some time.'

She was dying to know what connection he had with Queen Mary's School but she didn't dare ask. She'd never seen him look quite so angry before.

He was away for hours and didn't reappear. Shauna typed the letters he'd dictated, and then a special messenger delivered some legal documents which were entirely in Portuguese, and she began to translate them, enjoying the challenge of making sense of the formal and rather stuffy terms used.

At six, there was no sign of him, and at six-thirty she decided to call it a day. She took the documents up with her to the flat and had just placed them neatly on the dining-room table when she heard the front door slam and looked up to see Max.

She was torn between waiting to gauge his mood before she spoke and a very natural desire to demonstrate that she'd shown initiative in translating a complicated piece of Portuguese. Prudence lost.

'Hello,' she said. 'I worked until six-thirty. I've left the letters on your desk—oh, and these arrived...' She stopped in mid-sentence, suddenly aware that the bright green eyes were hard with anger.

'What is it?' she cried. 'What's happened?' But he didn't answer, just continued to stand there, staring at her.

'Max...' Even now, his name still sounded unfamiliar on her lips. 'What is it?'

There was a long silence. 'It's my daughter.' The deep voice was harsh. 'She's just been expelled from school.'

His daughter! Just imagining him as a father required a major adjustment in thinking, and she felt an unmistakable lurch in the pit of her stomach. If there was a daughter, then somewhere there must be a wife ... or an ex-wife ...

He carried on speaking as if she weren't there. 'Damn and *damn*!' he exploded.

She took a deep breath to steady her voice. 'What's happened?'

He stared at her. 'My daughter has what's euphemistically termed an "attitude problem". Her boarding-school have not taken kindly to the fact that she's been found smoking. Again.'

'And won't they reconsider?'

He shook his head. 'Nope. That's what the phone call was about this morning. That's where I've been all day. This was the "last chance", as they say.'

A daughter! She just couldn't imagine it. 'How old is she?'

'Thirteen,' he said automatically, and then must have seen her raised eyebrows. 'You don't think I look old enough to have a thirteen-year-old?' he queried. 'I was a child bride,' he finished sarcastically.

She wondered what had caused the bitterness in his voice. 'It's just that—well—I haven't noticed any photographs,' she faltered.

He turned abruptly and walked across the room to his bedroom and returned moments later carrying a large, silver-framed photo. He handed it to her. 'This is my daughter,' he said.

Shauna stared at the face of the young girl and realised that her mother must be very beautiful indeed, for, although the child owed her slanting green eyes to her father, Shauna saw that the

sculpted delicacy of her features had not come from
him. She found something strangely appealing in
the way the child stared defiantly at the camera, as
though daring it to make her smile.

'She's very beautiful,' she said.

'Yes,' he replied shortly.

For some reason which she didn't quite understand, she was reluctant to ask the next question.
'And—what about her mother? What does she
say?'

There was a long pause. 'She doesn't have a
mother.' He walked towards the drinks cabinet. 'Do
you want a drink?'

'No.'

He tipped some whisky into a glass and drank
half of it off in a mouthful. 'She's dead,' he stated
baldly, glancing up, the green eyes narrowed. 'It's
all right. You can spare me the platitudes. It all
happened a long time ago.'

She was mature enough to realise that he wasn't
lashing out at her, but his curtness hurt, nevertheless. She shifted in her seat a little, surprised at
his frankness, surprised that he should confide in
her at all.

'So what do you plan to do?'

He set the glass down on the cabinet, and began
to loosen his tie. 'They're sending her home
tomorrow. I'll have to find another school for her.
It's going to mean some disruptions. There isn't
room for her to come here, and anyway—it isn't
suitable. I have a house just outside Oxford, in the
country. There's no way round it—we'll have to

transfer the business down there, until I can get her into a new school.'

She noticed that he hadn't asked if she minded being uprooted, had just assumed that she would tag along, like a pet poodle, and perhaps he read something in her expression, for a frown appeared between the dark brows.

'Is that OK with you?' he asked grudgingly.

As a considerate question to his secretary, it barely registered on a scale of one to ten, but Shauna had a soft heart, besides which, objections from her were the *last* thing he needed right now. 'No problem at all,' she said. 'Go anywhere, that's me. I'm footloose and fancy-free, with absolutely no ties.'

He looked surprised for a moment, then nodded. 'Good. We'll leave first thing.' He hesitated for a moment. 'I feel I should warn you—she won't make things easy for you. She can be—very difficult.'

Like father, like daughter, thought Shauna, but she smiled at him. 'That's OK,' she said.

CHAPTER FOUR

'ARE you one of Daddy's mistresses?'

Shauna almost choked on the apple she'd been chewing. 'I beg your pardon?'

The green eyes met hers mutinously. 'I said, are you one of Daddy's mistresses?'

Shauna was determined not to look shocked which, she was sure, was the whole point of the exercise. 'I'm your father's new assistant. My name's Shauna Wilde.'

'Assistant!' The young voice was scornful. 'That's a new one! I suppose you'll spend all your time trying to get him into——'

'Bianca!' Max came into the room before she could finish the sentence, although it was perfectly clear to Shauna what she had been about to say.

'That's enough!' he warned his daughter. 'If you can't behave properly, you'll be sent to your room—and I mean it.'

'Yes, Daddy.' The child suddenly flashed her father a brilliant smile which illuminated her whole face.

Yet she was more than a child, thought Shauna. She was that volatile mix of child-woman, poised on the brink of adolescence. The photograph had not done her justice, she decided. It had not been able to accurately convey the almost porcelain-like translucence of her skin. She had tiny, neat wrists and limbs and looked sleek and well cared for. Only her troubled eyes betrayed her turmoil of adolescent emotions.

Shauna and Max had driven up from London that morning, and, after he had dropped her at the house, he had driven to the school to collect his daughter.

Shauna had been astounded to see Max's house—'Seekings'—a double-fronted Queen Anne building set in elegant and mature grounds. Now she could understand why the London flat was so bare, and so characterless. The flat was not a home—*this* was home.

It was full of beautiful old furniture, floors scattered with jewel-bright rugs, and impressive oil-paintings hanging on deep crimson walls.

Shortly after Shauna's arrival, a plump, old-fashioned woman appeared on the doorstep. 'I'm Mrs Roberts, the housekeeper,' she told Shauna. 'Normally I only work the weekends Mr Ryder's here, and when Miss Bianca's on holiday, but Mr Ryder rang me last night and said what had happened,' she explained, as she showed Shauna her bedroom. 'Sounded desperate, he did, poor dear. I know he'd like me here more often than I am, to keep my eye on her, and so on—but I've a husband to look after.' The smile on her tired face faded a little. 'Invalided from work now, he is.' Her voice dropped. 'She's a right handful is Miss Bianca. Had her own way for far too long, she has, and twists that father of hers round her little finger. A right handful.'

And Shauna, on coming face to face with the slight blonde creature, her elfin features doing nothing to disguise the rather worldly calculating expression in her eyes, would have tended to agree with Mrs Roberts. But she had been there herself. Once, she had been a lonely, confused schoolgirl, a little like this.

'I'll get the rest of the bags in,' said Max.

Shauna and Bianca watched in silence as he headed back towards the main hall.

Bianca's eyes flashed with pleasure. 'So are you sleeping with him, or not?' she demanded.

Shauna bit back the instinct to snap back. She was being tested, and she knew it. 'No, I am not,' she said firmly. 'And who on earth taught you to say things like that?'

'Oh, at school,' said the young girl airily. 'Everyone knows about sex at school.'

'Then it sounds as though you're better out of that particular school, doesn't it?'

'Except that me being here puts a spoke in the wheels, doesn't it? It means that I'll be forever playing gooseberry.'

'No, you won't,' said Shauna gently. 'I'm here to type and phone and translate, that's all—until your father sorts out a new school for you.'

The expression was truculent. 'Oh, yeah?'

Just at that moment Max came back into the room, and the conversation was brought abruptly to a halt.

'Mrs Roberts is just about to serve lunch,' he said. 'Do you want to freshen up, Bianca?'

'Sure. I know when I'm not wanted.' She strode out of the room, her hips swinging in a curiously adult way which only served to make her seem younger and more defenceless.

Max turned to Shauna. She thought how much older and wearier he'd become in the last twenty-four hours. There were lines around the bright eyes, lines which she foolishly found herself wanting to massage away with her fingertips.

'I'm trying very hard not to rise to those kind of remarks,' he said. 'I hope you'll understand that underneath that hard exterior there's the little girl I once knew trying to get out.'

She suddenly found herself wanting to reassure him. To tell him that she had no intention of sitting in judgement on his daughter. 'You don't have to explain anything to me, you know,' she said softly. 'I'm just here to do your work for you.'

He looked at her for a long moment, those strange, green eyes seeming as though they had the power to read her thoughts. The colour rose in her cheeks as for the briefest second she thought how near he was, how close his lips looked, and then she stepped back self-consciously. 'Did I hear you say something about lunch?'

'Yes,' he replied, still looking at her. 'Come through to the dining-room.'

The dining-room looked like something out of a film set. Three places had been set at the far end of the table, which sat in an alcove overlooking the gardens. There were fresh flowers on the gleaming wood, and crystal glasses and damask linen napkins. It was a long time since Shauna had experienced such correct formality, and she felt ridiculously underdressed in a simple skirt and soft grey sweater which matched her eyes. Max, she thought, would have fitted in anywhere—the fine quality of his clothes spoke volumes—and Bianca hadn't simply freshened up, she had changed out of her school uniform into a violet and green sweatshirt, with the shortest matching skirt that Shauna had ever seen. All of a sudden she felt like a poor relation.

'Isn't that a little short?' commented Max.

Bianca's voice was triumphant. 'You should tell that to some of your girlfriends, Dad. I thought you *liked* women who showed their legs.'

'That's enough!' he growled.

Shauna refused wine and poured herself a glass of mineral water, making a huge effort not to smile. *Touché*, she thought with amusement.

'Can *I* have some wine, Dad?'

'No, you certainly can't—will you please just eat your soup?'

After lunch, Bianca was taken into the study with her father, much to her disgust, presumably for a long and serious talk, thought Shauna, whose own afternoon was spent telephoning various contacts to alert them of the temporary change of address. The lines to Portugal were being unpredictable, and she spent a tedious half-hour waiting to be connected to Max's lawyer in Lagos.

While she listened to the interminable crackle of the international lines, she found herself thinking about Max's antipathy towards women. Well, that didn't tie in with all Bianca's comments about his 'mistresses' as she called them. But here again, a lot of men professed not to like women much—but that didn't stop them going out with them! Shauna banged a stamp firmly on to an airmail envelope with her fist. The subject of Max Ryder's conquests was taboo, to her at least. She wasn't going to make the mistake of her predecessor.

Dinner, though technically perfect, was a near disaster. The salmon mousse, the chicken Véronique and the *tarte aux pommes* might as well have been sawdust because Bianca alternately sulked and sniped at every available opportunity.

Shauna could see Max restraining himself from biting back an angry retort, and it seemed fairly obvious to her that they should have some time on their own.

She stood up. 'I'll skip coffee, if you don't mind. I'm going to turn in.'

Max's face darkened. 'Please don't feel you have to go because Bianca has decided to forgo good manners.'

Bianca scowled, and Shauna knew a wave of empathy. They were so alike, these two—both sitting there with angry faces—one so fair, and the other so dark, but both with those amazing green eyes. 'It's nothing to do with Bianca,' she smiled. 'It's more to do with being half-dead on my feet!'

Max rose, his face becoming a series of strange, shifting shadows as he moved out of the soft blaze of candlelight. A half-smile caught at the corners of his lips.

'Thanks for all your help,' he said, and Shauna felt as though he'd thrown her a bouquet.

'No trouble,' she answered. 'Goodnight, Bianca.'

'Goodnight,' came the sullen reply.

In the privacy of her bedroom, she untied the thick, dark curls and began to brush them in long, rhythmical strokes. She stared at her reflection in the mirror, the large grey eyes serious. Inadvertently, Bianca's presence had sparked off memories of her own childhood...

She was startled out of her reverie by a soft tap on the door of her bedroom, and she crossed the room to open it. A tall figure stood on the threshold.

'Max!' she said in surprise.

He seemed oddly hesitant. 'I wasn't sure whether or not you'd be asleep. I wanted to talk to you.'

She gave silent thanks that she hadn't changed into the silky nightdress which lay neatly folded on her pillow. She opened the door wider, in an automatically friendly gesture. 'Of course. Come in.'

There was an infinitesimal pause before he stepped into the room.

Hard to imagine a greater contrast than between the man and the room. The frippery of the predominantly feminine bedroom served only to emphasise his masculinity—the tall and muscular frame making everything seem fragile and insubstantial. She wondered fleetingly how many other women had made that gesture of inviting him into their bedrooms, and hoped that he would not misconstrue the meaning of hers.

He gestured to the window-seat. 'Do sit down. And don't look so afraid—I'm not going to bite you,' he growled.

'No.' It was hard to describe just what she *had* been feeling—but she certainly wouldn't have classified it as fear! She perched on the edge of the window-seat.

He remained standing and she had to strain her neck upwards in order to look at him. 'I didn't want to talk downstairs, where we could be overheard,' he began.

'By Bianca?'

'Yes.'

She gazed at him curiously, at his narrowed eyes, the taut lines around his mouth.

He began to move restlessly around the room, and it was several moments before he spoke, still in that fierce, growling voice. 'I know that she can be awkward,' he said abruptly. 'But it hasn't been easy for her.'

'I'm sure,' she agreed quietly.

He shot her a suspicious look, and moved to stare out at the dark night, his back to her, his stance unyielding. When he eventually turned round, the green eyes were flinty. 'I suppose that, like all women—you'd love to hear the gory details?'

She didn't rise to that one, taking instead the opportunity to dare to ask the question which had been foremost in her mind since yesterday. 'Has— has her mother been dead for a long time?'

His voice was flat. 'She died when Bianca was a baby. In a car crash.'

'Things must have been very hard for you both,' she said carefully.

He shot her a quick look, but, seeing nothing other than calm attention in her grey eyes, sat down at last on the seat next to her, the long legs out-stretched, his profile all hard lines. 'Yes, it was,' he said grudgingly. 'Very hard. Everyone assumed that I wouldn't want to keep the baby. My wife's family tried very hard to get me to give her to them. But I knew for certain that I wanted Bianca. She was the one good——' He hesitated. 'I wanted to keep her,' he said finally. The look he gave her did not invite questions. She got the distinct feeling that this was not something he often spoke of.

'The business was still in its very early stages,' he continued. 'But as I had started it up—and was working from this house—a nanny seemed the ideal solution. Not so,' he said wryly. 'It became a series of nannies. Bianca was a difficult baby, not sur-prisingly—who cried constantly. I clashed with the older ones who thought I was too soft with her. And some of the younger ones,' his voice sounded bitter, 'seemed less interested in caring for a small child than in bemoaning the lack of social life here in the village.

'I thought that things would improve when Bianca started school, and we could dispense with having these transient nannies. There would only be a few hours after school until I finished work when she would need someone to look after her—and Mrs Roberts agreed to do that.'

He moved the powerful shoulders in a small shrug. 'The trouble was that it didn't quite turn out like that—the business grew, and I was having to work later and later. Inevitably, my deals meant that I had to stay over in London and, occasionally, abroad. Mrs Roberts had family commitments of her own, and was unable to provide the kind of erratic care which Bianca needed—and neither was it fair to expect her to.

'The decision to send her away to school wasn't taken lightly—but I couldn't see an alternative. Bianca, perhaps understandably, saw the move as one of rejection.' His face darkened. 'And since then she has acquired quite a talent for getting herself thrown out of schools.'

'What kind of schools were they?'

He gave a humourless kind of laugh. 'Oh, I've tried them all, believe me. Progressive ones. Strict ones. Segregated. You name it, and I've tried them. Tomorrow I try again.' He shifted his position a little. 'It's late,' he said suddenly. He got to his feet, and, in an instinctive movement, held both his hands out to help her up off the window-seat. 'You look tired.' His voice sounded almost harsh. 'Get to bed.'

Breathlessly, she realised how close they stood, so close that she didn't dare look at him for fear that he might read the dizzying sensation of pleasure in her eyes, and she could have let him go on gripping her hands like that all night, if it weren't for the fact that any toe-curling feelings of pleasure were strictly one-sided.

As he bade goodnight to her, it occurred to her that he hadn't been a bit put out by having a long conversation with her in the privacy of her bedroom. A lot of men might have found it difficult to concentrate on what they were saying, given the implications of that.

But Max hadn't had the slightest difficulty concentrating, and why not?

Because he didn't see her as a woman, did he? She was just Shauna, his secretary. And a skinny kid, as he'd once said.

Oh, hell, she thought.

CHAPTER FIVE

SHAUNA slept deeply and a vivid dream came to haunt her. Through a warm mist a figure was trying to find her, but, each time she reached out, the figure retreated. She woke up with an empty feeling of disappointment, and, as she dressed in a simple black skirt, teamed with a crisp white blouse, she reflected that she had spent almost all her life alone.

What must it be like, she wondered, to wake up with someone beside you every day—to laugh with, to kiss, to make love with...? To do that with a man like Max Ryder? mocked a voice in her head, but she hushed it, defiantly dragging a brush through the wayward black curls.

Max and Bianca were already at breakfast, and they looked up as she walked into the sunny dining-room. Bianca's eyes widened as they saw her.

'Good grief!' she exclaimed. 'You look exactly like a waitress!'

Shauna flushed. Her outfit was serviceable and neat—but it *was* over three years old. She opened her mouth to defend herself, but Max had already butted in.

'Don't be so rude, Bianca.' The narrow green eyes swept up and down over her figure, as if he were seeing her for the first time. 'I'll give you an advance on your salary, and you can buy yourself some clothes.'

'That isn't necessary,' Shauna told him stiffly, beginning to feel like a scarecrow.

'I'm insisting,' he said firmly, and took a piece of toast from the rack.

'I could come and help you,' said Bianca gleefully.

Shauna smiled at this, as she sat down and helped herself to bacon and tomatoes. She could imagine what Bianca would try to make her buy! 'We'll see,' she said non-committally. Perhaps if they went on a shopping trip together, it might encourage her to be a little less hostile.

'Dad, what am I doing today?'

'The reading you've been set,' he growled, 'will keep you fully occupied, I imagine.'

'Dad—*please* could we have today off? Could we go riding? Oh, please, Dad!'

Max frowned. 'What you fail to have grasped, young lady, is that your presence here is not due to your old school granting you an unexpected holiday. You are here because you've been expelled. And if you think that I'm going to reward you for that by taking you riding, then you've got another think coming. Besides, I have to ring round all the schools.'

Shauna watched the girl's face. She had noticed the sullen, rather jaded expression disappear when she had asked her father to take her riding. All at once, she had seen the little girl behind the façade, breathless with excitement and anticipation. She took a deep breath.

'I could ring round the schools for you.'

Bianca shot her a grateful look, while Max directed a glare.

'This has nothing to do with you,' he scowled.

'Of course, the *last* thing I want to do is interfere,' she said meekly. 'I just thought that the fresh air might do you both good.'

There was silence for a few long seconds, then, unexpectedly, Max threw his head back and began to laugh. It was a totally uninhibited movement, and, as she stared at the firm column of his neck, the mushroom which she had been chewing suddenly lost all its flavour.

He lowered his head, and the green eyes met hers. 'You sounded just like my old matron,' he said gravely.

Great! she thought. If she wasn't being the skinny kid, she was being compared to some old battleaxe!

'I suppose,' he sighed, 'that, as I'm outnumbered, I shall have to gratefully concede.'

'Oh, Dad! Thanks!' A whirling, small blonde figure hurled herself at him, hugging her arms tightly around his neck.

Shauna felt a lump rise in her throat, and she stood up quickly, grabbing at two plates and stacking them on top of each other. 'I'll just clear these away, and then get started.'

'You don't have to do that,' said Max gently. 'Leave them for Mrs Roberts.'

'No, I'd rather help. Honestly.' She hurried from the room, not wanting them to see her own vulnerability at witnessing the unrestrained show of affection between daughter and father. Evidently, beneath the skirmishes of their relationship ran a deep vein of genuine love and regard—something which had been sadly missing from her own childhood.

She took the plates through into the kitchen where the big, old-fashioned stove gave out such a comforting warmth. Mrs Roberts, her hands full of suds, came towards her smiling, wiping the calloused red hands on to the floral apron.

'You shouldn't have done that!' she exclaimed. 'That's what I'm here for.'

'You shouldn't have to wait on me,' answered Shauna. 'I could grow to like it! Now, where's your dishwasher?'

'She won't let me buy her one,' said a deep, amused voice behind her.

The beautiful bone-china plates almost hit the stone-flagged floor, as Shauna turned round to face Max. He wore no tie, and a button of his shirt had come undone, giving Shauna a glimpse of the smooth brown skin of his chest, and she was reminded of that first night at the flat when he'd confronted her, the chest then completely bare, wearing nothing but those faded, half-zipped denims.

The memory completely drove all coherent thoughts out of her head. 'Pardon?' she said stupidly, thinking what a pity it was that he didn't smile like that more often.

'She refuses to have one near the place—a dishwasher.'

'And rightly so,' affirmed Mrs Roberts. 'Machines to do this, and machines to do that. Pretty soon, people will have forgotten how to use their hands.'

'As you can see—we're living in the Dark Ages here,' said Max, his head on one side, observing her. 'Thanks for offering to ring round the schools.'

Shauna put the plates on the draining board. 'Pleasure,' she replied. 'It won't take long to ask them to send us their prospectuses.'

'Good.' There was a pause as they walked out of the kitchen together, towards the study. 'You know, I get the distinct impression that I was out-manoeuvred by you at breakfast.'

She feigned surprise. 'Who—me?' she enquired innocently.

He laughed again. He had been doing rather more of that than usual this morning, she noted. 'We'll be back in time for lunch.' He hesitated, his eyes skimming the black skirt which hung just below her knees. 'Your salary's on the desk in my study. Use it.'

Quite why this should have flustered her so much, she didn't know. She wished that the skirt had been shapelier. 'I'll do that,' she said hastily.

His expression was thoughtful. 'I'd better go and change.'

She walked slowly into the study, thinking that working for him was perhaps not going to be as easy as she had anticipated. Not if he was going to be so—so *charming*. Was this how it had started with the last girl? she wondered. Had he begun to trust her, to confide in her? Had he let his guard slip? Only to find that the loyalty of an employee had suddenly turned into unwelcomed and un-asked-for love? As long as she was careful not to make the same mistake. He was not looking for love. Hadn't he told her that himself?

She worked all morning, busying herself with phoning round schools, having to break off now and then to speak on Max's behalf to lawyers in Porto Mâo who were dealing with the purchase of the golfing complex.

Mrs Roberts brought her tray of coffee at eleven—steaming, fresh and strong—accompanied by a small plate of florentine biscuits.

Shauna leaned back in the chair, and smiled. 'Thanks, Mrs Roberts. You're spoiling me.'

'You make sure you eat them,' said the house-keeper. 'You're all skin and bone.'

If anyone else said that, she'd scream! And anyway, she wasn't *that* thin. Her waist and hips may have been slender, but her bust more than made up for that. It was the bane of her life.

At twelve-thirty she left the study to wash her hands before lunch when she met Max and Bianca in the hall. It had obviously been a successful outing, because they both looked relaxed and happy, and Bianca was bubbling over with good humour. She spied Shauna.

'Oh, Shauna!' she enthused. 'It was *fantastic*! Really great! Dad, have I time for a shower before lunch?'

'Definitely,' he replied, pretending to wrinkle up his nose.

Bianca bounded away, taking the stairs two at a time, and Shauna was left alone with Max. He had obviously ridden his mount very hard, for the thick, dark hair lay in tangled wet waves plastered to his head. His forehead was beaded with sweat, and the light shirt he wore beneath his riding jacket clung to his torso.

There was something so raw—almost primitive—something so ridiculously and overwhelmingly *masculine* about him, that she started trembling, and couldn't stop.

'You're not cold, are you?' he enquired assessingly.

His response killed her reaction instantly. Perhaps the 'skinny kid' should take to wearing thermal vests, she thought ruefully. 'No, I'm not. But you will be—if you don't get out of those clothes.'

Now what had she said? She flushed scarlet. 'I didn't mean——' she stuttered. 'That wasn't a proposition.'

His gaze was very steady, his face serious, but there was a hint of laughter flashing in the green eyes, a trace of humour uplifting a corner of the firm mouth. 'Really?' he said softly. 'You *do* disappoint me, Shauna.' And then he left, leaving his secretary dry-mouthed and weak and *angry*, too. What the hell was he playing at? He'd warned her off, and yet now he was teasing her, flirting with her, playing with her emotions as a cat would a mouse. And he wasn't stupid. He must know perfectly well how lethal his own particular brand of charm was, exercised deliberately like that.

As her pulses slowed to normal again, a fleeting fear crossed her mind. Please God, she prayed. Don't let me fall in love with Max. Don't let me become another victim of that cold and unfeeling heart.

At dinner that evening, Bianca did not come down.

'She's tired after her ride,' explained Max. 'She had soup and toast in the kitchen with Mrs Roberts, and is at present listening to some awful row on the radio, and drinking a mug of cocoa. All of a sudden she's beginning to look like a young girl again, and not a pastiche of older women she's seen in fashion magazines.'

Shauna felt unaccountably nervous as her earlier fears came back to haunt her, sitting alone with him at the gleaming table, the candles casting strange shadows around the room, as Mrs Roberts brought in dish after delectable dish. She drank more wine than she had intended, or than she was used to, and as its warmth flooded through her veins it washed away every tension.

They chatted in desultory fashion, and had just finished the cold lemon soufflé when he leaned back in his chair, eyeing her speculatively.

'No ties, hmm?'

She blinked. 'I beg your pardon?'

'You. You told me you had no ties. I'm interested to know why.'

She tried, without success, to shrug her shoulders nonchalantly. 'It isn't much of a story.'

He frowned. 'I can't believe you don't have anyone.'

'Well, I don't.' Her voice shook slightly in spite of her bravado. 'My parents were divorced when I was nine. My father went away, and we never saw him again. It broke my mother completely. I looked so like him, you see—and she couldn't bear to have me around.' She twisted the stem of the wine glass between long, slim fingers. 'So she sent me away to boarding-school.'

'As I did with Bianca, you mean?' His voice was harsh.

Her grey eyes surveyed him calmly. 'No, Max. Nothing like that. Circumstances forced you to send her away. My mother didn't want for anything materially—she could easily have kept me at home. She *just didn't want me*,' she emphasised, and, pushing her chair back, she walked over to the spitting glory of the log fire, crouching down to warm her hands in front of it, so that he couldn't see her face.

'Go on,' he said.

She found herself wanting to tell him. She gazed into the flickering flames. 'I was a lonely child, even at school. Always daydreaming. I think I used to retreat from the reality of my life by living in a fantasy world. My mother's visits to me were— infrequent, to say the least. It was a bit of an embarrassment, at school, how little she cared.' She forced herself to sound bright, not to betray any of the pain which had dominated her school-days.

She turned to face him again. 'I had no idea what I wanted to do, really, but, as I'd been brought up speaking Portuguese, Spanish and French, languages seemed the obvious choice. Then my mother remarried.' She paused as she saw the question in his eyes.

'Oh,' she shrugged. 'He was no evil stepfather figure. Harmless and innocuous enough, but we had nothing in common. I was in my first year at university, when the news came that the plane carrying my mother and stepfather back from their holiday had crashed. It's funny—even if you've had a bad relationship with your mother, it can still hurt like hell when she dies.'

'I'm sure,' he agreed quietly.

'When the will was read, it transpired that they had indulged themselves royally and had built up a mass of debts. The house had to be sold to pay them.' He was looking as though he wanted to hear more, she thought. 'Consequently, I was fairly broke at college. I worked at night, weekends—you know the kind of thing.'

'Must have been hard?'

She flashed him a smile. 'Not really. I was lucky to be there. And when I finished—I took off to see a bit of the world.' She wished he'd stop looking at her like that. Didn't he realise that that crooked half-smile, the unexpectedly tender softening of his eyes, made her want to curl her fingers possessively around those strong hands? To feel him as close to her as he'd been last night?

'So what made you come back?'

She shrugged, the thick swaths of black curls surrounding her oval face like a dark cloud. 'You can't keep drifting forever. Sooner or later you have to settle down. And it might as well be now.'

'Oh, Shauna,' he said suddenly, softly.

She rounded on him furiously. 'Don't say it like that! Just don't! I don't want your pity!' The sudden movement caused a rippling movement of the silky blouse across the swell of her breasts and she saw his gaze drawn to it.

Something in the room had changed. A sensation as tangible as electricity crackled in the air. He tore his gaze away from her breasts, and their eyes met, and locked.

Her tongue darted out to lick her lips—fear, or something very like fear, had dried them, had set her heart racing, her pulses hammering. She heard his sharp intake of breath.

'I don't want your pity,' she repeated weakly.

'It isn't anything remotely like pity that I'm feeling right now.' He stood up in an abrupt movement which caused his chair to scrape roughly against the polished floor. It sounded deafening. She thought that he was about to walk out, but she was wrong, for he walked towards her, slowly and deliberately, until he stood looking down at her, his eyes burning, a message in them she couldn't read, or perhaps she could—for she moved forward at the same time as he pulled her tightly into his arms, his hands spread possessively across her back, her face buried in the warm masculine scent of his shoulder. She didn't know whether he intended to pacify or to stir her, but she found herself pressing or being pressed against the hard length of his body, her body moulded into his as if glued there. She looked up and their eyes met for the briefest of moments and then he bent his head and swiftly, almost brutally, began to kiss her.

His mouth tasted sweet, and of wine—soft, hard, tantalising, demanding, and her lips opened welcomingly beneath its pressure. He pulled her even closer, and she became breathtakingly aware of the muscular strength of him—every sinew and every fibre. She thought that she felt his hands flutter towards the heavy and achingly sweet straining of her breasts, but it might just have been the frantic beat of her heart.

In a deliciously heady haze she instinctively moved her hands from his shoulders to thread her fingers into the glorious blackness of his hair, when he pulled himself away from her as brutally as he had begun. His breathing was ragged and his eyes looked black in the candle-light, and haunted.

'Dear God!' he exclaimed. 'Dear God in heaven! What the hell am I thinking of?' and he thrust her away from him.

Her senses screamed their mutiny and, her heart still racing, she stared at him, thoroughly confused by his reaction. 'What—what is it?' she stumbled. 'What's wrong?'

He met her gaze, his face a tight, angry mask. 'That should never have happened.' He muttered something indistinct under his breath and strode to the door, leaving her still reeling as she listened to him mounting the stairs with an angry step, while she found herself incapable of any movement, other than a weak collapse into the armchair behind her.

CHAPTER SIX

SHAUNA stumbled up to her bedroom when she was certain that Max was no longer around. Automatically, she stripped off her clothes and pulled a white gauzy nightgown over her head.

She stared back at her reflection in the mirror, at the glittering eyes and flaming cheeks. She lifted cool fingers to wonderingly touch her lips, now dark and swollen from the pressure of that heady kiss.

Was it simply because it had been—so long? When had she last been kissed? A year ago, maybe—with Ramón, the Portuguese doctor she'd dated briefly. But it hadn't been like *that*. Nothing like that.

Max's kiss had set her on fire. She had responded to him with a stunning eagerness and lack of inhibition, and then he had ruined everything by his horrified reaction to finding her in his arms.

Oh, hell, she thought as she climbed into bed. What on earth was she going to say to him tomorrow? Worse still, what was he going to say to *her*?

Sleep, not surprisingly, eluded her until the first light of day had begun to creep around the curtains and consequently she awoke feeling headachy and grumpy.

She should have stopped him, she definitely should have stopped him. But he was just as much to blame. He had been the one who had made the first move. It had been he who had crossed the room and grabbed her in that almost brutal way. True, she hadn't exactly put up a fight—but he had been the instigator, not she.

Her bravado disappeared as she slowly descended the elegant, curving staircase. Let's face it, she thought, if Max Ryder had decided that she was just another eager little secretary with the hots for him, then she would be out of the door and sent packing as fast as you could whistle.

She heard footsteps.

'So there you are!' said an accusing voice, and a neat blonde head peeped out from behind the study door. 'I've been waiting for you for ages!'

The greeting was so friendly, so unexpected, and so unlike the stormy reception she had been anticipating, that she started, having to hold on to the heavy oak banister for support. 'Oh, it's you, Bianca! You startled me.'

Bianca ignored this. 'You look terrible.'

'Thanks,' said Shauna wryly.

'No, I mean—you've got big black shadows underneath your eyes. You and Dad haven't had a row, have you?'

Shauna's heart sank. 'Why do you say that?'

'Well, you look like death, and Dad went storming out of the house, first thing, looking furious.'

And she knew what had caused that fury. 'Did he say where?'

Bianca looked at her out of the corner of her eyes. 'Only that he'd be back tonight.'

'Tonight?' Why hadn't he said something? Was he so embarrassed by last night that he couldn't bring himself to talk to her?

'So you'll have to look after me, won't you?' Bianca's voice was wheedling.

Shauna shook her head. 'I can't,' she said flatly. 'I have to work.'

'But it's Saturday!' said Bianca triumphantly. 'Nobody works on Saturday, do they? And besides—we're going shopping.'

Shauna put her head to one side, so that a dark plait fell forward over her shoulder. 'We are not.' With that determined set of her mouth, Bianca looked uncannily like her father, she thought.

'Oh, but we must! Dad's given you an advance and you've got to get some new clothes——'

'I am not in the mood for shopping.' In all honesty she felt like crawling back to bed and hiding under the sheets for the rest of the day.

Bianca's smile was winning. 'Don't say you can't drive?'

This, coming from a thirteen-year-old! 'Of course I can drive!'

'Well, then. The car's in the garage—I can direct you into town. And besides,' the green eyes, so like her father's, were suddenly watchful, 'what else are you going to do with me all day, if you don't take me shopping?'

Shauna hesitated. Put like that, a shopping trip seemed like the better option. Blast Max, she thought. He might have been angry with her, or with himself, but that was really no excuse to disappear—leaving her in the role of baby-sitter to a child she hardly knew, and who had a reputation for being capricious. Still, a shopping trip might at least take her mind off recent developments.

She nodded her head. 'Oh, very well—you win! I take it I've got time to drink some coffee first?'

'Sure,' grinned Bianca. 'I'll go and get changed.'

Shauna had never driven a Range Rover before, and she eased it up the drive with care, reflecting on how strangely enjoyable it felt to have this excited teenager beside her, keeping up a cheerful running commentary as they drove towards the nearest town.

'That's where I rode my first mare. And that's where the Cheriton cows escaped and blocked the road for *hours*.' She pointed to a large, grey-stoned house. 'And that's where Rupert used to live. His mother still does.'

Shauna changed gear. 'Who's Rupert?' she asked casually.

'He was Daddy's friend. And Mummy's. My godfather. Oh, look—it's one of the Denver twins on his bicycle—I think he's gorgeous. Can you slow down, please?'

'No, I can't!' Shauna laughed, deciding that her boss's daughter was more like thirteen going on thirty!

They parked in the multi-storey car park, and Shauna was suitably impressed by the new, brightly lit precinct, with all its shops under one roof. Any reservations she had begun to have about such an impromptu shopping session quickly disappeared, simply because Bianca didn't give her a chance to change her mind! She steered her with great res-

olution in through the glass doors of a shop she
would never normally have gone in, and, within
minutes, had pulled out a selection of garments.

'You should *never* wear drab colours,' Bianca
announced. 'With your hair and colouring you
should have bright clothes.'

Shauna found it slightly shaming that a thirteen-
year-old should be so knowledgeable about what
suited her, and the lethargic sales assistant, who
didn't seem particularly interested in any kind of
selling, looked up to heaven on more than one
occasion.

'How do you know so much about clothes
anyway?' grumbled Shauna, as she pulled a cherry-
red cashmere dress down over her hips.

'Daddy says I inherited it,' announced the child
proudly. 'Because Mummy was a model—before
she had me, anyway.'

Shauna was totally unprepared for the un-
reasonable flash of resentment that this piece of
information produced. A model? She stared in the
mirror. 'I can't wear this,' she said suddenly. 'It's
far too short.'

'You've *got* to have it,' said Bianca decidedly.
'You've got legs all the way up to your armpits. In
fact,' she screwed up her eyes a little, 'you don't
look bad at all.'

'Thanks a bunch!'

'Don't mention it!'

But her mood lifted again as she bought leg-
gings, two sweaters, the cherry wool dress, and a
black cotton jersey dress which she wasn't at all

sure about, but which Bianca convinced her that she *had* to have.

After lunch, more shopping and then a film, it was dark by the time they walked back to the car and drove home companionably.

'Are you really not interested in my father?' asked Bianca suddenly.

Third gear was reached with a horrible grating sound. 'Why on earth do you ask that?'

Bianca shrugged. 'Well, you said you weren't the other day——'

'And I meant it,' interposed Shauna hastily. 'He's my boss, Bianca. End of story.'

Bianca moved one moccasin-covered foot up on to the dashboard. 'Pity,' she sighed. 'He never meets anyone like you normally.'

'I'm not sure I like the sound of that!' Shauna laughed. 'What kind of people does he usually meet, then?'

'Oh, you know—rich ones. Beautiful ones,' she said gloomily.

'Well, that's the biggest backhanded compliment I've ever heard!'

'I didn't mean it to be. The women he meets— well, they always smile at me with their mouths, but never with their eyes. They see me as an obstacle, you know.'

Shauna's heart went out to the girl, suddenly looking so young and unsure. 'I'm sure you're imagining it,' she said gently. 'I bet they like you really.'

The young voice affected uninterest. 'They don't. They just pretend to when Dad's around. But I don't care.' There was a pause. 'Shauna—can I tell you something?'

'Blast!' The headlights picked out the startled gaze of a rabbit, and Shauna swerved just enough to miss it without risking an accident. By the time they had recovered, she remembered that she had halted the girl in mid-flow.

'Sorry, Bianca—what were you saying?'

The girl shook her head. 'It doesn't matter now. We're almost home.'

Shauna thought that Bianca seemed increasingly tense as the big car crunched up the gravelled drive. She could see the study light on, and Max's car parked at the front of the house. I'll collect the bags later, she thought, as she jumped down from the driver's seat. Bianca was still strangely silent, and, as Shauna put her front key in the lock, the heavy door was yanked open from the other side, and she had to struggle not to topple inside.

Max was standing there, his face a study in anger, the eyes narrowed to slithers of icy jade, his hands resting on the lean hips, his legs apart.

'Where the *hell* have you been?' he demanded, and Shauna shrank back from the fury in his voice.

'I——' began Bianca.

'I am speaking to Shauna,' he said coldly. 'I assume that she was the one driving the car. You'd better go to your room, Bianca, until I send for you.'

With what sounded like a strangled sob, Bianca tore up the stairs.

She could hear his breathing, coming fast and heavy. She steeled herself not to remember how similar it had sounded last night, after they'd kissed, but faint colour had washed into her cheeks before she could block the thought out completely. What on earth had made him so angry?

'You'd better come into the study,' he ordered, and she followed him automatically, too stung and confused to formulate a coherent question.

In the study he turned to face her. The only light in the room came from a lamp on his desk, and the intensity of its glare was concentrated in a small area, leaving the rest of the room gloomy and shadowed. In this light, the blackness of his hair and the dark shadows on his face made him look almost demonic. She stared back at him.

'Where the hell have you been today?'

It was a struggle not to sound defensive, and yet, she thought, she hadn't done anything wrong. 'I went shopping,' she said. 'With Bianca. You told me I could use the car any time. We had lunch, saw a film, and came home, that's all.'

'That's all?' He sounded incredulous. 'You don't think it matters that you disappear with my daughter for most of the day? That I arrived back this morning to find you both gone, and sat around all day not knowing where you were, worried sick? And you say "that's all"?'

Her confusion cleared immediately, and the import of his words became crystal-clear. Bianca, for whatever reason best known to herself, had lied to her. Had tricked her into taking the car into town and disappearing for the day. But it was up to Bianca to admit that to her father. She wasn't going to tell tales, not when he was in *this* kind of mood.

'I'm sorry if you've been worried,' she began, but his words cut across her.

'What right did you have to countermand my orders?' he interrupted. 'Perhaps you thought that whetting my appetite with your attempts at love-making last night would give you some position of authority?'

She gasped aloud at his words, but he carried on as if he hadn't heard her.

'Or maybe you play a cleverer game than that.' His smile was the most ruthless she had ever seen. 'If you think that befriending my daughter is the route to my heart, then don't bother. As a ploy it's been used before.'

It took a few seconds for what he was saying to her to sink in, and the disbelief became hurt, and then anger. Her voice was shaking, and the words bubbled out hotly like boiling toffee.

'How *dare* you?' she demanded. 'Just how do you dare? I can't even believe that you'd think it! Suggesting that I was nice to your daughter be-cause in some way I thought it could get to you. Of all the arrogant, unforgivable things to say!' She glared at him furiously. 'I don't know what has made you quite so cynical about women—but haven't you considered that your warped view of humanity is actually *damaging* to the child? Don't you think that she's picking up on all your dis-torted values? Is that what you want? Tell me, Max Ryder—do you want a child who trusts no one? Just like you?'

His face had gone white and he opened his mouth as if to speak, but she was there before him.

'Well, don't worry. I won't be here to see it. I don't want to work for a man like you. I won't live like this, and I'm giving you notice. I shall be leaving in the morning.' And, saying this, she turned and ran.

She almost scrambled up the flight of stairs to her room, and, as she leant weakly against the door, she realised that she was shaking like a leaf. Legs which felt as though they had been carved from wood took her over to the bed, with its frilled and flounced canopy, and slowly she sat down.

So that, she thought, was that. The best opportunity she'd had to make something of herself was now a thing of the past, but all the perks in the world could not compensate for the monstrous things he had accused her of. A huge salary was one thing, but she could not and would not tolerate living in such a climate of mistrust and hostility.

She must have been mad not to even consider that Bianca had not been telling the truth. She had walked into that little trap as willingly as the fly to the spider. Why should the girl suddenly have undergone such a remarkable change in attitude? She, Shauna, had been ridiculously naïve.

But she had taken Bianca at her word—and was that such a terrible thing? Because hers was a trusting nature, in spite of all the knocks she'd had. In spite of her parents, and her being orphaned at a relatively young age, her soul had remained intact. Unlike *his*.

Her face burned with anger and shame as she recalled the look on his face as he'd spoken of her 'attempts' at lovemaking. *Attempts*? What was he implying? That they'd been deficient in some way? She allowed herself a grim smile. He was a liar. She had enjoyed it, and *so had he*.

She was wearily thinking about packing her things together when there was a tap at the door. She made no answer. It would either be him or his daughter, and she had no inclination to see either of them.

The knocking resumed.

'Go away!' she called.

The voice was deep and curiously resigned. 'No. We need to talk.'

The smouldering resentment which she still felt was temptation enough for her to fling open the door and meet his gaze with one of belligerent stubbornness.

'What for? Haven't you said enough already?'

'Please,' he said, quite gently.

One word, but a word which she guessed he'd used very little in his life. A word which, when spoken in that soft tone he'd adopted, pushed all the fight out of her.

'What do you want?' she asked, in a small, defensive voice.

He stood just inside the room. 'I've just been speaking to Bianca,' he said, still very quietly. 'She told me the truth—that she'd conned you into believing I'd gone out for the whole day and left you to look after her. Why the hell didn't you tell me what she'd said?'

'Because you didn't ask.'

'But you let me believe that——'

She held her head very high, her eyes on a level with the chiselled lips. 'No,' she contradicted. 'You believed what you wanted to believe. You'd already made your mind up, hadn't you? And what would you have had me do? Tell you that your daughter had been lying? Expose her to the kind of fury which you vented on me? Is that what I should have done? No way, Max. I'm big enough to stand up to bullies, but she isn't.'

A muscle began working furiously in his cheek; his face beneath the tan had gone almost grey. She'd gone too far.

'I'm sorry,' she said. 'I shouldn't have said that.'

He stared at her. 'Why not? It's the truth, after all.'

There was a pause as Shauna struggled to find the right words. 'I've an idea, if you'd like to hear it,' she said tentatively.

Dark eyebrows disappeared, his mouth a tight line. 'The magic solution?'

She ignored the sardonic note in his voice. 'I think that Bianca getting herself expelled and deliberately fooling me into playing hookey with her—knowing just how much it would annoy you—is all a form of attention-seeking behaviour. I'm just trying to imagine how she must see it. She doesn't get to see you very often, so she's deliberately naughty—and that gets her your undivided attention. It's not good attention—but it's still attention.'

He gave an impatient wave of the hand. 'So what are you saying I should do? That I should move the company down here permanently and send her to the local day school? That's as unworkable now as it was five years ago.'

She looked at him steadily. 'Can I make a suggestion?'

His mouth twisted wryly. 'Suggest away. Solve my problems for me, Shauna. Wave your magic wand.'

Her idea had all the brilliance of simplicity. 'What about weekly boarding?'

He frowned. 'What?'

The words came spilling out in her eagerness. 'I mean—you may have already given it some thought, but it strikes me as an ideal compromise. Find a school as close to here as possible that takes weekly boarders. Bianca will board mid-week, while you're in London—and come here every weekend. It'll give you more time together.'

His expression was one of mocking surprise. 'The first woman who has ever suggested I spend *more* time with my daughter, rather than less,' he said sardonically.

She didn't offer a comment on this, but the tight line of her mouth registered her disapproval.

'You don't think she'd find that disruptive?' he asked. 'Neither fish nor fowl, not fitting into one place or the other?'

'I think it's just what she needs,' Shauna said quietly. 'At my school, we all thought that the weekly boarders had the best of both worlds.'

There was a long pause. She saw a light flare in the green eyes, and momentarily the harsh, tense lines on his face disappeared. 'I'll look into it tomorrow.' He stood up slowly and looked at her. 'You will stay?' he asked.

She stood looking at him, knowing that she would stay. The perfect job, she thought wryly—there was no such thing. Certainly not *this* job, anyway—and Max Ryder was the reason why. He was the antithesis of the perfect boss. He could be difficult, moody and autocratic, she knew that.

Yet as she stared at the hard, enigmatic face, she discovered that it was easy to ignore the voice in her head which was clamouring to be heard. The voice which was asking her if she was being entirely truthful about her motives for staying. She pushed aside the nagging question of how much her growing feelings for Max were affecting her decision. Sometimes feelings should be left well alone, not analysed out of existence.

She gave a small nod. 'Yes, Max. I'll stay.'

CHAPTER SEVEN

IT WAS a bright, clear morning and Shauna breezed downstairs in a light-hearted mood which matched her outfit. The jade-green angora sweater which she wore over her jeans echoed the swinging hoops at her ears, and the jet-coloured curls were caught up at either side of her head by combs of exactly the same shade of green.

As she walked into the breakfast-room, Max lifted his head, looked at her very hard, and frowned slightly.

'I've got a smut on my nose?' she hazarded.

He shook his head. 'You look—nice,' he commented. 'That's all.'

The compliment was hardly lavish, but it made her feel ridiculously pleased, so she took refuge in teasing. 'Nice?' she giggled. '*Nice*? And this coming from a man who once berated me for using the word "adequate"!'

There was a glint in the green eyes. 'OK, then—you look better—than you used to.'

Now why should that half-baked compliment fill her with a silent, frustrated rage? Surely it wouldn't have hurt him to have hunted around his not inconsiderable vocabulary for something more flattering than 'better'. Unless, of course, that was all he thought she *did* look.

All she knew herself was that she looked rad-
ically different from the girl she had been when she
first arrived. Oh, the difference a slick of lip gloss
made! And, taken in hand by the undoubtedly talented Bianca, she had discovered that dressing up
could be quite fun. The drab clothes had been
bundled up and donated to the local thrift shop,
and Shauna had decided that she would never look
back!

It was hard to believe that the shenanigans of a
fortnight earlier had ever occurred, such was the
air of ordered calm which had descended on the
household.

After Max had left her that night, a tearful
Bianca had come to her room.

'Please don't leave,' she had sobbed. 'I'm so
sorry I lied to you.'

Shauna had heard her out, and had then gently
pointed out that her behaviour was going to hurt
no one more than herself in the end, and would
drive a wedge between her and her father.

At last, a place as a weekly boarder was found,
and Bianca professed herself delighted with the
scheme. The best news as far as Bianca was concerned was that the new school didn't want her to
start until after Christmas, as it was felt it would
be too disruptive to begin mid-term.

'She's going to go to her grandparents in Scotland
on Boxing Day until term starts,' Max had told her.
'So we're incarcerated here until then.'

Which, as far as Shauna was concerned, was like
winning the pools. She loved the work and she loved
the countryside. She would have liked to have

thought that her relationship with Max had altered since all the disruptions, but no such luck. The most it seemed she could hope for was the kind of grudging respect he had demonstrated when she helped him pull off a remarkable deal ahead of a rival, but, other than that, he gave little of himself away. Polite, yet curiously distant—he remained the most unfathomable man she had ever met.

They worked together in the mornings, and in the afternoons he usually left her with more than enough letters to occupy her, while he went riding with Bianca.

She grew used to living with him, but her reactions to him were unpredictable.

Once, she had walked into the kitchen to be confronted by his back view as he leaned over the table, reading a newspaper. Thankfully, he didn't notice her for a second or two, and she stood rooted to the spot, dry-mouthed, riveted by the sight of faded denim clinging to and moulding the narrow lines of his hips.

Did he always have such an effect on women? she wondered. Such a *physical* effect? She'd never experienced anything like it before, and it had started to trouble her. The memories of him, and her unique reaction to them, had begun to haunt her at night when she lay alone in between the exquisitely laundered lawn sheets. Sleep had become an elusive creature which she pursued hopelessly as she tried to blot out the stormy yet nebulous dreams which left her feverish and confused when she awoke with a start from them.

Quite apart from anything else, they were together so *much*. From breakfast until bedtime. And still it wasn't enough for her. She found herself resenting it when he drove to the nearby town without her. In bed at night she listened for his footsteps when he mounted the staircase to his bedroom, her heart foolishly racing as she heard them pause—or was she just imagining them pausing?—then its beats subsiding into agonised disappointment as they passed by to his own room. It was playing havoc with her nerves.

Perhaps it would be better when they returned to London, she reasoned. She could catch up with her old college friends, and gradually forge a new life for herself, so that she only saw Max at work.

So why was she dreading that moment so much?

She had already observed with wry amusement that Max's full-time occupation of Seekings seemed to have spread around the county, since invitations for him began to flood in. Her only comfort came from the fact that he didn't seem overjoyed by his popularity.

At breakfast one morning he eyed the pile of cards at his place with disgust. 'Damn these society matrons!' he snapped, as he began to slit the envelopes open. 'I refuse to endure being introduced to their giggling daughters.' His expression altered slightly. 'Oh—here's one for you, Bianca.' He scanned the letter before handing it over to his daughter.

Bianca read it eagerly. 'Oh, Dad, it's from Sally Bartlett—we used to have riding lessons together.

Remember? She's invited me to go over for the day to see her new pony—oh, can I, Dad?'

Max smiled. 'I'll ring her mother later.' He caught her expression. 'I said *later*. I'm not promising anything.'

Bianca was dropped off at Sally's the following morning, and when Max returned he walked into the study to find Shauna typing.

'Get your coat,' he instructed. 'We're going out.'

'Out?' Her grey eyes lit up.

'Bianca isn't here—it's an ideal opportunity to drive to Bristol to talk to my accountant. I rang to confirm last night.'

'Oh. Right.' She was furious with herself for feeling so let-down. Just what had she been expecting? A cosy lunch for two?

During the hour's journey to Bristol, Max, predictably, was silent, putting a Beethoven tape on the superb stereo and playing it very loudly—and its thunderous strains matched Shauna's mood very well.

The accountant's office was situated in a quiet back-street of the city. On the wall outside 'T. W. Entwhistle' was engraved on a discreet bronze plaque.

Max pushed the bell. 'It'll be useful for you to hear the financial side of things. Try and pick up on the main points and remember them.'

The fairly humble exterior of the building was deceptive. Inside it was luxuriously well-appointed, with subdued wall-lights and several small glass bowls of cut flowers. A smart brunette at the desk stood up as soon as Max walked in.

'Hi, Max! I was sent out for pastries and told to make lots of strong black coffee,' she smiled.

Shauna found herself wondering if this kind of treatment was given to *every* client. Somehow she doubted it.

'It smells good,' murmured Max appreciatively. 'Thanks, Katrina.'

'And I'm to show you straight in.'

'Good. This is Shauna Wilde, my secretary.'

The two women nodded at one another, and Shauna followed them along a narrow corridor where Katrina lightly tapped the door and held it open.

'Mr Ryder,' she announced.

Shauna was partially hidden by Max and was grateful for this when she saw the woman behind the desk get up and walk towards him, her hands outstretched to grasp his.

'Max,' she smiled.

'Hello, Trudy.'

It was impossible to read anything in his voice and Shauna wondered why she should be so surprised that Max's accountant was a woman. After all, lots of women were accountants these days, though she doubted whether many of them looked like Trudy Entwhistle. She was superb—with sleek hair the colour of polished mahogany caught into a sophisticated chignon, out of which not a single hair protruded. The slim and obviously well cared for body was clothed in a cotton jersey dress of pristine whiteness which, though neither low-cut nor short, contrived to cling to every slender curve.

Sooty-lashed brown eyes regarded her directly. 'Hello,' she said coolly.

Max moved aside. 'This is Shauna Wilde—my new secretary. Shauna—meet Trudy Entwhistle, my accountant.'

'How do you do?' said Shauna politely.

'A secretary?' queried Trudy, looking her up and down. 'Lucky you, Shauna!' Tiny white teeth were bared in a smile. 'It must be wonderful to have a job which carries no responsibilities. What I'd give,' she sighed, 'to be able to knock off at five o'clock every night without a care in the world.'

'Shauna works hard enough,' said Max, amusement in his voice.

Trudy turned to him. 'I'm *sure* she does. Come and sit down, Max. Shauna, could you pour the coffee?—it's on the side.'

Shauna gave an imitation of a smile which turned into a grimace. She was certain that Max saw it, but, frankly, she didn't care. Pour the coffee! Just who the hell did Ms Trudy Entwhistle think she was? She'd like to pour it all over the expensive rug which lay in the centre of the room!

However, she opted for the dignified option, which was to up-end the pot into the tiny china cups and hand them out.

While she sipped, Shauna attempted to do as Max had asked—to listen and to store up information— but this proved harder than expected since Trudy Entwhistle seemed hell-bent on clarifying just how long, and how intimately, she'd known Max.

Shauna thought that she would stand up and *scream* if she heard Trudy's confident voice say

again, 'You remember that, Max, surely—that was
the day...' The sentence would then be completed
haltingly, and with a good deal of eye contact and
soft, gurgling laughter. She was so *obvious*, thought
Shauna scornfully—although she had to admit that
once she got down to business she was very good
indeed. Shauna listened as she rattled off a stream
of information, then sat back and smiled at Max.

'I had a phone call from Harvey Tilton's accountant. Did you know that he, Harvey, Harvey's
son and their wives are touring England? And that
they're in the Cotswold area for the next few days?'

Max nodded. 'Yes, I phoned him last night after
I spoke to you. I'd originally planned to entertain
him on the London leg of his trip, but I explained
the circumstances and now we're going to meet up
while they're in Oxford. They're coming to Seekings
for dinner on Saturday.'

Trudy gave a slow smile as one slim leg was
crossed over the other. 'And do I assume,' she said,
looking directly at Max, her eyes widening with
pleasure, 'that you'd like me to take over my usual
role—as your hostess?'

Shauna felt slightly ill as she tried not to imagine
just *what* duties Trudy performed as hostess, when
Max's next words astonished her.

'No, thanks—Shauna's going to do that.'

Which was the first *she'd* heard about it!

'Oh, is she?' said Trudy, looking at Shauna with
cold eyes.

Max glanced at his watch. 'We won't take up any
more of your time, Trudy.'

They all stood up and Trudy turned to Shauna.

'I'm sure you'd like to freshen up,' she said, with a smile which stopped short of the brown eyes. 'I'll show you where.'

In the wash-room, Trudy turned to her, an expression of mock concern on her face. 'My dear, let me give you a tip or two. You don't stand a hope in hell with Max if you wear your heart on your sleeve, the way you're doing.'

Beads of sweat breaking out on her forehead, Shauna put her wrists under the cold tap. 'I don't know what you mean,' she muttered.

A shrug of the elegant shoulders. 'His last secretary fell in love with him and paid the price. When *will* you girls realise that you can't just marry the boss and be carried away on his white charger? Men like Max want their women to be achievers, not hangers on.' There was a parody of a smile on the glossy pink lips. 'And with all due respect—a man like Max isn't going to have much in common with a typist, now is he?'

Shauna turned the tap on full and a jet of water sprayed out, covering both women with little droplets of water.

'Oh, I'm so sorry!' she babbled, grabbing a handful of the green paper towels and dabbing at Trudy's spotted white dress. 'Here, let me.'

'Get *off* me,' said Trudy, between gritted teeth.

Max made no comment when they reappeared, but an eyebrow rose into the dark hair.

Trudy gave him three kisses on alternate cheeks and, amid entreaties that he call her, they left.

He was silent for a while in the car, and so was Shauna, still thinking about Trudy Entwhistle. Was she really being transparent about the way she felt for Max? Or was Trudy just suspicious of any woman Max associated with? There had been something about the familiarity with which she'd treated Max that had made it very obvious that they'd once been lovers. And were they still? Max turning down Trudy's offer to help him entertain suggested otherwise.

He broke the silence. 'You know Harvey Tilton's an American I've done a lot of business with?' he asked.

She nodded. 'He has an option on twenty-five per cent of the villas in the new complex?'

'Right.' There was a pause. 'Feel up to playing hostess?'

She was still smarting from his accountant's gibes. 'But if Trudy's used to entertaining with you—she might be a better choice?' she hinted recklessly.

He glanced at her. 'Trudy is a brilliant accountant,' he stated, not answering her question at all.

She'd need to be, thought Shauna. She sure as hell wasn't talented at industrial relations! But then Max pushed a cassette tape into the player, which eliminated any further conversation.

Shauna was secretly delighted to play hostess, even more so when Max left the menu to her. So the 'typist' knows *something*, she thought, as she sucked the end of her pencil and tried to imagine what Americans would most like to eat in an English home.

On the evening of the dinner party, Bianca helpfully ate early and disappeared to her room to watch television.

Shauna dressed carefully in a short electric-blue silky dress with a cross-over bodice, and was standing admiring Mrs Robert's beautifully laid table when Max came slowly down the stairs dressed for dinner, and her heart gave an alarming thump. She had never seen him dressed formally before and the black jacket echoed his dark hair. She thought that the trousers had been cut by a genius, or perhaps it was just his physique which set them off—the soft cloth couldn't quite disguise the muscular thighs beneath. Remembering Trudy's comments, she tore her eyes away and started re-folding a napkin.

The Americans arrived promptly and Shauna was introduced to Harvey Tilton and his wife Connie—a fit-looking couple in their forties—together with his son Brett and fiancée Patti.

'Pleased to meet you, Shauna,' grinned Harvey, as he pushed a towering replica of himself towards her. 'Brett's being groomed to take over from his daddy—so he'll probably drive us mad by picking Max's brain all evening and talking about nothing but finance!'

Shauna laughed, finding the American's friendliness infectious. 'I don't mind a bit,' she insisted.

Harvey mimed shock. 'Say! A beautiful woman who likes business—no wonder Max has hidden you away down here!'

'Harv-ee!' said his wife. 'Stop that! You're embarrassing Shauna.'

It was true. Shauna felt herself blushing to the roots of her hair and was fortunately distracted by Patti asking who had made the floral centrepiece— but not before she had seen the corner of Max's mouth lift very slightly in a sardonic expression which spoke volumes.

The other couple who made up the group were Harvey's accountant 'Buzz' Arnold and his wife. Buzz was in his late twenties, a good-humoured man almost as tall as Max, and Shauna thought that his wife Wendy looked as if she had been reared on orange juice and sunshine—she looked so healthy— with lightly tanned skin, gleaming white teeth, and a fall of sun-streaked hair to her shoulders.

Max moved round the room to pour the champagne. When he reached Shauna, her hand shook very slightly. He steadied her glass. 'I'm waiting to see you blush again,' he murmured.

'Don't hold your breath!' she snapped, furious with him for drawing attention to it.

They ate the delicate canapés which Mrs Roberts had brought in.

Dinner was almost ready when the telephone started ringing. Shauna looked at Max. 'I'd better get that,' she said. 'Mrs Roberts is just about to serve the soup.'

'Take it in here,' he said shortly.

It was Portugal and Max's lawyer there needed a subtle point of clarification to be made on a contract. Shauna knew what Max had intended, and spoke animatedly in her fluent Portuguese. When she had replaced the receiver, she found their guests staring at her.

'Wow!' said Connie. 'That was *brilliant*, honey! Imagine being able to speak Portuguese—why, Harvey and I can barely get our act together to order two Cokes!'

Shauna smiled. 'It's easy for me—I learned to speak it when I was little.'

'And is Portuguese the only other language you speak, Shauna?' asked Wendy.

There was a small silence. Shauna, slightly embarrassed at all the attention, opened her mouth to reply, but someone was there before her.

'Heavens, no,' came a wry voice. 'Shauna speaks four, at the last count—don't you?'

She looked at him quickly, but there was no answering stare which might have told her just what he was thinking. Instead, his mocking smile was for the whole company.

She heard Harvey's aside.

'You've sure got a gem there, Max.'

And the dry reply.

'Haven't I?'

The scallop soup was received with lavish praise.

'Your choice, honey?' Connie asked Shauna.

'Naturally,' replied Max urbanely.

'But Mrs Roberts cooked it,' butted in Shauna. 'She's an excellent cook.'

The good food and the company were making her settle back and really enjoy the evening. If only Max would relax a bit, she thought, instead of keep giving her those curious looks.

Although he chatted charmingly with his guests, she got the feeling that he was apart in some way—

observing things, observing her—and always with that slightly sardonic, mocking smile.

Not that Harvey and his party seemed to have noticed, or perhaps they were used to Max and his cool manner—they certainly bubbled over with more than enough enthusiasm to compensate for any lack of his.

Saddle of lamb was next, with vegetables from the garden.

'This is a truly *British* meal,' enthused Wendy. 'Mrs Roberts should come and cook in our hotel.'

'They have what they call an "international" menu,' explained Connie. 'We keep telling them— we haven't come all the way to England to eat French or Italian food!'

Max had told Mrs Roberts to leave after the main course, and Shauna was in the kitchen getting the lemon meringue pie out of the oven when she heard someone come in the kitchen behind her. She was unable to turn round because of the hot dish in her hand, but she immediately felt the unmistakable presence of Max even before she heard the deep, drawling voice.

'So when's the cabaret?' he enquired, leaning back against the wall, his hands in his pockets, regarding her.

'I *beg* your pardon?' She put the pie carefully on the Aga and turned to face him. As always, the enigmatic face was a mystery to her.

He gave a half-smile. 'Well, this *is* the Shauna Wilde show tonight, isn't it? I'm thinking of laying odds on who'll come out with the next profuse compliment. Brett is currently expressing the

opinion that you're wasted as my secretary—the last
suggestion was that the United Nations might be
suitable recipients of your combined linguistic
talents and good looks. I just hope we aren't going
to have his fiancée marching out on us!'

'That's not fair!' protested Shauna. 'Brett's just
being charming—that's his way—they all are. And
I certainly didn't intend for him to be anything other
than that.'

The green eyes glinted. 'No, you didn't, did you?
You don't go looking for compliments, do you,
Shauna? You just get them. And there's the rub—
you're completely oblivious to it all.'

His remarks puzzled her. She couldn't decide
whether or not he was disapproving, and she was
absolutely certain that Brett had eyes only for his
beautiful fiancée. Nevertheless, she chatted almost
exclusively to Patti during coffee and found her delightful company.

'I've seen the most *beautiful* wedding gowns in
a shop in Oxford,' she confided to Shauna. 'I'm
half tempted to buy my dress here and have it
shipped back home.'

'Oh, no! Not weddings again!' Harvey winked
at Shauna. 'That girl's got a one-track mind—all
she ever wants to talk about is weddings!'

'Ignore him,' smiled Connie at Patti.

'Well, maybe Shauna wants to talk weddings,
too,' interjected Patti, then leaned forward. 'How
long have you and Max been living together,
Shauna?'

There was a moment of awful silence. Shauna
was appalled, feeling her face flame and then

blanch, looking to Max for some light-hearted comment which would erase the unintended *faux pas*, but there was none. He continued to sip his brandy with remarkable composure, as though the comment had just washed over him. Which no doubt it had, she thought bitterly. People probably made assumptions like that about Max all the time.

It was left to Harvey to break the silence, but with a suggestion which Shauna could have done without.

'Hey!' he exclaimed. 'It's been a great evening— what say we roll up the rug and end it with a dance or two?'

Everyone enthused over the idea, bar Shauna and her boss, but Harvey took over and put some dance music on with alacrity. The two married couples immediately and unselfconsciously began to dance, and Shauna managed to escape from the room to put some more coffee on.

She returned eventually and was coaxed into dancing in turn with Harvey, Brett and Buzz, and it was impossible not to relax and enjoy herself again with their good-natured chatter. Warm-faced and laughing, she was about to go out again to refill the cream jug, when Harvey caught her by the shoulders.

'We can't have this!' he exclaimed. 'A pretty girl not dancing and, much as I'd like to monopolise you all night—I guess I ought to give the only single guy in the room a chance!'

Shauna caught a glimpse of Max's face. 'Oh, no—really...'

Harvey smiled. 'Don't think he's going to take "no" for an answer, honey.'

And, true enough, Max was moving towards her, his face resigned, perhaps realising, she decided, that it would be impossible for him to refuse to bow to the collective pressure of everyone urging him to dance.

He certainly didn't look as if he were looking forward to it, she thought, feeling ridiculously flustered. It was easy to snap confident rejoinders at Max when he wasn't standing a warm, brandy-scented breath away, waiting to take her in his arms, which was, presumably, why her response made her sound about the same age as Bianca. 'I don't—I mean—you don't have to,' she stumbled.

He laughed then. 'I know that,' he said, and put his arms lightly around her waist.

She could scarcely breathe and he'd hardly touched her. She fought for an excuse which would save her from discovery. Any minute now and she was going to blurt it out—how much she cared for him, cherished him, and wanted him. Any minute . . . 'I'd better go and see to the coffee,' she said desperately.

'Shut up and dance,' he smiled, and pulled her into his arms properly.

Her body moulded itself into his as though it had been designed for only that purpose. She had her hands on each of the broad shoulders, her head bent, the curls hiding her face—but she could feel his breath, and his heartbeat.

She let him lead her, her reservations vanishing as she experienced the sheer joy of being held by him. The sweet throb of desire had her in its thrall, so that when he tightened his hold even more, making some soft muffled noise at the back of his throat, she could no longer resist—even if she had wanted to. She knew that he was slowly dancing her out of the room—away from their guests and the music—but the music was unnecessary for the particular dance they were creating. She should go back to the others, she thought fleetingly, but she was powerless to move away from him.

They found themselves in the study where only the silvery moon—suspended like a giant football outside the window—illuminated the pale oval of her face.

They stopped and she continued to let her head hang down, until he pushed her chin up with the tip of his forefinger, so that their eyes met at last.

'Are you going to look at me now?' he said softly, and the finger moved to trail slowly along the outline of her mouth, which instantly began to tremble. And then, as she had somehow known he would all along, he bent his head to kiss her.

It was nothing like that first kiss. Nothing. That had been short, almost brutal, hard, and somehow desperate. This was an explicitly sensual kiss, slow and deliberate, and every second of it—from the start when his tongue traced tiny circles on her bottom lip, to when it moved with exciting intrusion inside her mouth—told her in no uncertain terms that he wanted her.

She was in his arms, being kissed to death, and he was moving with her until he had her pushed up against his desk. He leaned over her, so very dark and muscular, dominating her utterly, and, as one taut thigh thrust forward, her legs parted automatically to accommodate it.

She felt his hand slip inside the silky material of her dress to move it aside and she trembled as he found her breast, touching and massaging it through the lace of her bra. She could feel the tip, painfully alive with pleasure, straining against the thin material, and the lace irritating her, constraining her.

She had her hands coiled in his hair, but she inadvertently dug her nails into his scalp as she felt his other hand brush lightly over her stomach, and down further, to enticingly circle the soft flesh of her thigh. And when one finger moved to brush lightly over the line of her panties she found herself wantonly pushing against his hand, a tiny cry wrenched from her lips.

She began to stroke her hand over the fine lawn of his dress shirt—spreading her palms luxuriously and possessively over his chest, hearing the small sigh of pleasure which escaped his lips as she did so. And then he found the front clasp of her bra, unclipping it easily, so that her breasts spilled out, and he bent his head to take one swollen tip into his mouth, his tongue erotically teasing it so that it throbbed with a spasm of pleasure so intense that she felt she might buckle and faint, and her hand went out automatically to support herself, colliding instead with the telephone—and there was a loud crash as it hit the parquet floor.

Max terminated the kiss immediately, and, as she heard him swear, she turned her face up to him, seeing anger in the green eyes as he released her.

He stood looking hard at her, shaking his head, and she could hear the disbelief in his voice. 'What are you doing to me?' he exclaimed. 'You're my *secretary*, for God's sake! Do you realise that we've got guests—*guests* in the next room?' he said savagely, and then his voice dropped. 'I must be out of my head.'

She was still too shaken, too aroused to speak, and he must have seen it, for he looked down at her, taking in her flushed cheeks, mussed hair and her disarrayed dress.

With a small sigh, he quickly refastened her bra and pulled the bodice of her dress straight again. 'You're in no state to go back in there,' he said. 'It wouldn't take much for them to figure out what we've been doing.' He shook his head again. 'Unbelievable,' he said, as if to himself, before picking the phone up and placing it back on the desk.

'You'd better go to your room,' he muttered. 'I'll make your apologies for you.' And with one movement, his hand pushed through his hair to leave it as unruffled as if he'd done nothing more than walk out into the lightest breeze. And without another word, or further look, he walked coolly from the room.

CHAPTER EIGHT

IT TOOK several minutes for Shauna's limbs to stop shaking sufficiently for her to make her way silently upstairs to her bedroom, her thoughts in turmoil as the reality of what had just happened hit her. She and Max had been petting like teenagers while important clients were dancing only yards away. Just imagine if Harvey or his wife or any of the party had come after them.

She groaned as she turned on the taps to run a bath—*now* what would happen? She scrubbed at her body in the bath as if by washing every inch of her she could wash away the memories which would not leave her.

But when she came to soap her breasts, she felt that restless yearning begin to invade her once more, as she recalled his hand, stroking and caressing her, extracting little ripples of pleasure from her responsive body. Her flesh burned where he had touched her, just as if he had taken an iron and branded her with fire.

She buried her face in her hands despairingly as the suspicions of the past few days resolved themselves into one truth so blindingly clear that she must have been a fool not to have realised it before. She was in love with him. This overwhelming sensation which had thrown the rest of her life into grey insignificance—this was love. In spite of all the warnings from people like Trudy—and disregarding his own wishes—she had committed the sin of her predecessor and fallen in love with Max. But it was up to her to make sure that he didn't realise—or even guess at it—because he had made it quite clear from the very beginning that he didn't want her—not in that way, anyway—and if she were to ever coexist with him again she must be prepared to forget it had ever happened. The question was whether she would be able to do that.

And how was Max going to react when he saw her? Would he simply be able to shrug it off as he had done tonight—as a minor aberration on his part, but nothing to get excited about? Or would he find such intimacy intolerable for their future working relationship? She remembered the way he had said 'What are you doing to me?' It had sounded like an accusation. But surely he couldn't blame her? Hadn't they both momentarily lost control?

The next morning was Sunday and she stayed in bed late, knowing as she did so that she was delaying the moment of reckoning—her confrontation with Max.

She dressed in jeans and a cherry-coloured sweater, brushing the newly washed hair and then catching two long strands at the side with red slides. The red contrasted vividly with her hair, making her look strangely exotic, and, as she went slowly down the stairs, she wondered what the scenario for today would be.

For the last few Sundays, the three of them had breakfasted together. Max and Bianca had gone riding, while Shauna read the papers, and after lunch they had all gone striding through the woods, ending up in the library, playing Scrabble and doing justice to one of Mrs Roberts's enormous teas. Somehow, she couldn't see that happening today.

She was right. As soon as she walked into the breakfast-room, she saw that Max was not wearing the faded jeans and rather shabby sweater he normally wore for riding, but an elegantly cut suit, with a pale blue shirt which lay silkily flat against the broad chest. Bianca sat opposite him, a belligerent expression on her face.

'Good morning,' said Max formally. 'What would you like for breakfast?'

The sight of the kidneys and bacon, the dish of scrambled eggs and the rack of toast suddenly filled her with nausea. This was not, she realised, going to be as simple as she had imagined. 'I'll just have coffee, thanks.'

He poured her out a large cup of the strong, fragrant brew and handed it to her.

'Thanks. Not riding this morning, Bianca?' The child hadn't looked this miserable for ages, she thought.

'No,' said the girl sullenly. 'Dad's going out.'

She met his gaze with a question. 'Out?'

She thought he looked uncomfortable as he pushed his half-empty plate away from him. 'I have to go to Cheltenham for the day. As it's Sunday, I wondered if I could prevail on you to look after Bianca for me? You can have a day off in the week to make up for it, of course.'

She tried not to flinch. He couldn't have rein-
forced her position as an employee more surely if
he had written it on the walls in letters ten feet high.
'Of course I don't mind,' she said stiffly. 'Looking
after Bianca is a pleasure, not a chore.'

The green eyes narrowed. 'Thank you.'

She met his gaze mutinously. 'You're welcome.'

'Of course, Dad only goes to Cheltenham for one
thing,' Bianca sniped. 'He's going to see Marta.'
She turned to glower at her father. 'Aren't you?'

A chord of memory struck. A low, husky voice
on the telephone—ages ago, at the London flat.
That had been Marta, Shauna recalled.

'I will probably be seeing Marta, yes. Not that
it's any of your business, young lady. You'll have
a fantastic day with Shauna, you know you will.'
He pushed his chair back and stood up.

She watched as he bent to kiss his daughter and
was offered a very cold cheek in return. She took
a huge mouthful of coffee and scalded the inside
of her mouth as she strove to act unconcerned. Unconcerned, her left foot! Who the hell *was* Marta?

Shauna stood outside the breakfast-room as
Bianca leaned on the front door jamb, waving
goodbye as he roared away in his Mercedes. She
saw dejection written into the set of the girl's
shoulders, and impetuously she ruffled the thick
blonde bob.

'What would you like to do today?' she asked.

Bianca shrugged. 'I don't really care.'

Shauna put an arm round the narrow shoulders
and squeezed them. 'Oh, come on—your every wish
is my command.'

This produced a grin. 'You can't ride, can you?'

Shauna shuddered. 'Horses—yeuk! They terrify the life out of me!'

'Just what *can* you do?'

'Walk?'

Bianca laughed. 'I guess we'll walk, then!'

Wrapping themselves up in boots and thick coats and hats and scarves, they took sketch-pads and pencils and a big bag of stale bread to feed the ducks, and drove to a local beauty spot.

The morning was brightly clear, the grass crisp with frost which looked like icing sugar. They had been walking for about a quarter of an hour when Shauna did exactly what she had spent the last fifteen minutes vowing she would not do.

'Who's Marta?' she asked casually.

Bianca kicked at a stray pebble with some gusto. 'She's Daddy's number one mistress.'

Shauna frowned. 'You mustn't use that word,' she reprimanded automatically. It had been precisely the answer she had been expecting but it still made her heart sink like a stone.

Bianca turned candid green eyes to her. 'Well, she is. A mistress goes out with a man for all the things she can get out of him, like money and jewels, doesn't she?'

Shauna felt she was skating on very thin ice here. 'Er—yes.'

'Well, there you are, then!' crowed Bianca triumphantly. 'They're only interested in Daddy's money—they wouldn't go near him if he wasn't rolling in it.'

Shauna had been about to say that Max Ryder had far more to recommend him than mere wealth, but she stopped herself just in time. 'Your father is entitled to choose who he likes as friends, and he has a right to expect you to be polite to them,' she pointed out gently, wishing that she'd never started this conversation.

'Sorry,' Bianca sighed. 'Marta is Daddy's girlfriend.'

Shauna walked straight into a muddy puddle without noticing. 'Oh,' she said, in a small, empty voice.

'Well, that's what she likes to call herself. Daddy calls her his "friend". Whenever there's a party or a "do" he nearly always takes her, if she's not away working. She's often abroad. She's a model,' she confided.

'Oh,' said Shauna faintly, wishing that she hadn't asked, wishing that her stomach would stop sinking like a runaway lift.

Bianca kicked at another stone. 'I hate her. When Daddy's around she's all sweetness and light, but as soon as he goes out of the room it's "Bianca, *do* stop slouching", or "Isn't it time you went to bed, Bianca?" '

'I'm sure she's very nice, really,' said Shauna lamely, wondering how much of Bianca's rebellion lay in the fact that she obviously didn't hit it off with her father's partner.

'And I don't know why Daddy describes her as his "friend", when I know they sleep together.'

'Bianca!' Shauna was suddenly glad that she'd eaten no breakfast because there would have been no guarantee that it would have remained in her stomach, and she was angry with herself for the turn the conversation had taken. 'You mustn't say that—you don't even know if it's true.'

'Oh, yes, I do—because she told me.'

Shauna stood stock-still, aghast. 'She actually told you?'

Bianca nodded. 'Daddy wasn't there. He'd have been furious. She was yawning, and she said, "That's your father's fault—he kept me awake nearly all night", and then she giggled. Yeuk! I think she only said it to make me jealous.'

'But Bianca,' interposed Shauna gently, 'why should she want to do a thing like that?'

'Because she thinks that Daddy won't marry her because I wouldn't accept her as a stepmother.'

'And is that true?'

Bianca grinned. 'Too right! I'd hate her to be my stepmother—I wish he'd marry you!'

Shauna took hold of Bianca's shoulders and crouched down so that their eyes were on a level. 'You may wish it, Bianca—but it isn't going to happen. Wishing doesn't make something come true. I'm just his secretary, that's all.'

They spent the whole morning tramping around the countryside, Shauna striding out with fierce determination, as if by keeping herself occupied she could prevent herself from thinking about what Bianca had told her...

She dreaded going back to the house, at having to face him. Knowing... Knowing what? That he'd spent the day in another woman's arms? Perhaps allowing him the freedom to caress her as he pleased

last night had whetted his appetite for fulfilment.
Her cheeks burned with shame in the darkness.

As they approached the house, there was indeed
a car parked at the front, but it was not Max's
Mercedes. Shauna jammed the brakes on. Oh,
please don't let him have brought her here, she
prayed. Not that.

'Recognise the car?' she asked Bianca.

Bianca shook her head. 'No idea. Oh, goody—
we hardly ever get visitors.'

Shauna realised that she was playing for time as
she helped Bianca out, convinced that the car must
belong to Marta, and that she and Max would be
sitting cosily by the fire in the sitting-room, or,
worse still—in his bedroom.

She started to get the key out of her handbag,
but Mrs Roberts must have heard them, for she had
opened the door and was standing there, an odd
expression on her face.

Bianca ran in. 'Whose car is it?' she demanded.

Mrs Roberts stood looking at her. 'You've got a
visitor,' she said unnecessarily. 'It's Mr Hamilton.'

'Rupert!' yelled Bianca excitedly.

Rupert. Shauna blinked. Now where had she
heard that name before?

'Uncle Roo!' Bianca squealed. 'Oh, yummy!
Where is he?'

'I'm right here,' said an amused voice. 'What a
wonderful reception from my favourite god-
daughter.'

'Your only god-daughter,' protested Bianca, and
then she ran and hurled herself into his arms with
all the speed of a young gazelle. He scooped her

up into his arms, and then, over the top of her head, he saw Shauna—still standing in the shadows—for the first time.

He put Bianca down and looked at her. 'Well, well, well,' he said slowly.

Shauna looked back at him. He was just a little taller than herself, and very slim. His face wore the deep tan of the ardent skier and this made his blue eyes seem even bluer. He was dressed in a beautifully cut jacket underneath which she could see a soft cashmere sweater which matched his eyes perfectly. His hair was blond—very blond—and tumbled in a fashionably cut style around his neck.

He had the kind of confidence and magnetism which were natural by-products of money and breeding.

The blue eyes flashed with interest. He extended an elegant hand. 'Rupert Hamilton,' he smiled. 'Who's *enchanted* to meet you.'

CHAPTER NINE

'WELL, well, well,' Rupert said again. 'Who have we here? A mysterious black-haired beauty who doesn't speak.'

Shauna, who had so psyched herself up for a confrontation with Marta, smiled at him. 'Hello,' she said.

'This is Shauna,' announced Bianca. 'She's Daddy's new secretary—and she's great.'

Aristocratic-looking eyebrows were raised. 'A secretary, you say? And one who seems to have won the affection of the dreadful young Bianca. My, my!'

Shauna, deciding that she ought to start asserting herself as an intelligent adult, and not as some dumbo, held out her hand to him. 'I'm Shauna Wilde,' she said. 'And I'm very pleased to meet you.'

He took her hand and lifted it very slowly and deliberately to his lips, holding it there while he held her gaze with heavily lashed eyes, in such an overly theatrical gesture that it would have been laughable had it not been so effective.

'Enchanted,' he murmured. 'Max always did have the most impeccable taste, but you, my dear, are quite a refreshing change from the rather *outrée* type he usually favours.'

Shauna reflected, as she tugged her hand away, that everyone she met seemed to take great delight in telling her how unlike the beautiful women Max usually associated with she was. She turned to Bianca.

'Why didn't you tell me that your godfather was coming over?' Or, more importantly—why hadn't Max?

Bianca frowned. 'Because he never tells me. And anyway, he hardly ever comes to visit.'

Shauna raised her eyebrows but said nothing. Now why, she wondered, was that?

'Now, now.' Rupert ruffled Bianca's hair playfully, and shrugged expressively at Shauna. 'It's because I'm such a busy man.'

'Busy going out to parties,' giggled Bianca. 'Did I tell you we saw you in a magazine at school, Uncle Roo?'

'Good picture, wasn't it?' he smiled.

'I'm afraid that Max isn't here,' Shauna began, remembering with a pang just where he was. 'We're not expecting him back until late.'

Bianca tugged at his arm. 'What are you doing here, Uncle Roo?'

He twitched his nose. 'I'm visiting my dear old mama for Christmas.'

'So that means we'll be able to see *lots* of you! Oh, good-oh!' exclaimed Bianca delightedly.

'Does Max know you're coming?' asked Shauna.

The blue eyes had suddenly grown very cold. 'Hardly. There isn't much love lost between Max and myself. I expect you've found how perfectly impossible he can be?'

Well, she had. But she wasn't about to start telling this man about it, and being disloyal to Max. Not, she thought, that he deserved her loyalty. She pushed the thought, and the mental pictures of him cavorting with some stunning model, away, and turned her attention back to the present.

'Will you be staying for a while? For tea...?' She found herself in the odd position of hostess.

Rupert smiled and walked over to Mrs Roberts, who had remained listening to the entire conversation. 'I'd love some of Mrs Roberts's famous fruit-cake.' He put his arm around the shoulder of the plump housekeeper. 'Even though she didn't offer me any herself.'

Mrs Roberts, looking unusually disgruntled, shook the elegant arm off as if had been a fly. 'Oh, go away with you, Mr Hamilton—that's enough of that. I'll get you your tea, though it's more than my job's worth...' She marched off in the direction of the kitchen.

'Bianca, why don't you take your godfather into the sitting-room, while I go and help Mrs Roberts?' Bianca, at any rate, seemed genuinely fond of Rupert, thought Shauna, even if he didn't rate too highly with Max or Mrs Roberts!

Rupert was eyeing her speculatively. 'Oh, Mrs Roberts can manage,' he said airily. 'Why don't you come into the sitting-room with us, Shauna, and let me run my fingers through those delicious black curls?'

There was something so outrageously over-the-top about him, that Shauna laughed aloud. She shook her head. 'Better not—I can hear Mrs

Roberts muttering from here—I'd better go and
help her.'

She ran lightly into the kitchen, where Mrs
Roberts was banging cups and saucers on to the
silver tray. Shauna took them from her. 'Here, let
me,' she said. 'You'll smash them like that.'

The older woman unwrapped the rich fruit-cake
from its covering of greaseproof paper. 'He isn't
going to like it,' she declared darkly.

'Who isn't?'

'Mr Max. Likely as not, he'll hit the roof when
he comes back to find *him* here.'

Shauna privately thought that the housekeeper
was making Max sound like some Victorian despot!
Surely he couldn't dislike his daughter's godfather
that much? Anyway, it was absolutely nothing to
do with her, and she wasn't about to start taking
sides. And personally, *she* thought that the blond,
beautifully spoken man seemed perfectly charming.

And wasn't it actually rather pleasant, she
thought, to have someone new around the house?
Someone, moreover, who was giving Bianca a great
deal of pleasure.

They had tea, and during it Rupert regaled them
with stories and scandals about the aristocratic
world he inhabited. At nine o'clock, Bianca was
packed off to bed with the promise that she could
see Rupert the following day. Shauna came downstairs from saying goodnight to find him warming
his hands in front of the fire. He had removed his
jacket and had lit one of the smaller table lamps.
Without the jacket, he looked less imposing and,
therefore, less threatening, and there was, thought

Shauna, something not unflattering about having a rather attractive man heap compliments on you. Particularly when your ego had taken such a battering recently.

He turned round as she entered, running his left hand through the thick blond curls in an unconscious gesture of preening. 'I suppose I'd better be going,' he said. 'Unless you're allowed to offer a poor traveller a drink? Or wouldn't Uncle Max like it?'

She hesitated. Well, why not? she thought defiantly. Why not have a drink with a perfectly nice man who had spent the whole afternoon making them laugh. She could just imagine how *Max* had spent the afternoon.

'What would you like?'

'A whisky and soda. Shall I do the honours? I think I can still remember where the drinks cabinet is. Can I get you one?'

She usually drank wine, but she couldn't really ask him to open a bottle just for her, so she nodded. 'Just a small one, please.'

She decided that his idea of a small one and hers must have been two entirely different concepts because when she took a mouthful she nearly spat it out, it tasted so bitter, but she didn't want to seem gauche by asking him to weaken it—particularly as he had just started to tell her about the time he'd met Elizabeth Taylor. So she quietly drank the Scotch, and listened.

By ten, she felt just a little bit merry, and he had persuaded her to put some music on the compact-disc player.

'It's too late,' she giggled. 'I don't want to wake Bianca.'

'We won't—we'll turn the volume right down low. Come on—you must! There'll be balls galore this Christmas and I haven't danced in ages—and as I've got two left feet you've to help me practise.'

Put like that, it sounded like fun, although she thought that he must have been exaggerating his lack of prowess because it was obvious he was a very accomplished dancer, even though he held her far closer than she would have liked. Trying to keep the atmosphere light, Shauna wriggled a little to try to relinquish Rupert's hold on her.

'Goodness—you're a sexy little dancer under that air of innocence, aren't you?' he laughed.

'Yes, she is, isn't she?' The voice cut through the music like a knife slashing through silk, and she looked up in horror to see Max standing in the doorway, surveying the scene before him with open contempt on his face. He took in the whisky-filled glasses and the ruffled cushions on the sofa, and Shauna realised how it must look through his eyes, remembering in horror how her dance with Max had ended with her half-naked in his arms. She was about to move Rupert's vice-like grip, but Max's words beat her to it.

'If you get any closer, you'll be in danger of asphyxiating her,' he drawled, a cold ring to his voice. 'Perhaps you'd like to put her down now?' It was a question which brooked no answer other than the affirmative.

Rupert stepped back dramatically, his hands raised in mock supplication. 'It's swords at dawn,

I suppose?' he exclaimed, looking to Shauna for support, but she dropped her eyes to the carpet, embarrassed.

For answer Max advanced slowly across the room, a kind of black fury on his face. Shauna saw Rupert blanch beneath the golden tan, and he began backing away, until eventually Max almost had him pinned up against the wall, his face just a few inches away.

'You know, Max—you could teach the SAS a thing or two...' Rupert's voice tailed off as he met the icy green eyes.

'What the hell are you doing in my house?' Max hissed, in a soft voice which only seemed to emphasise the cutting edge of his tongue.

'I'm here to see my god-daughter—it *is* allowed, you know.'

Max looked around the room in mock search. 'Then where is she? I can't see her.'

'She—she went up to bed a little while ago,' interposed Shauna, with a slightly desperate ring to her voice.

He didn't even acknowledge that she had spoken, merely carried on talking in that dangerously flat voice. 'So while the cat's away...? Tell me, Rupert—while my daughter slept, did you think that you'd make it doubly worthwhile and seduce my secretary while you were about it?'

'But it wasn't like that!' cried Shauna.

He met her gaze for the first time, the narrowed eyes slowly flicking over every inch of her body, and she had to suppress a shiver as she met his critical gaze. 'No?' he queried softly.

She realised that one of the combs which had kept a mass of the dark curls off her face must have somehow become lost, and that her eyes were bright and glittering, her cheeks all flushed—due to the unaccustomed whisky, no doubt. She looked like a woman who had been interrupted in the early stages of lovemaking—while nothing could have been further from the truth.

Rupert was looking from one to the other with interest. 'Why, Max,' he said slyly, 'I do believe you're jealous.'

He was rewarded with a look which could have frozen at ten paces. 'Don't tempt me, Rupert. I'm about two seconds away from planting my fist in that pretty face of yours.'

The blond man gave a nervous laugh. 'But you can't stop me from seeing Bianca, can you? I *am* her godfather, and you did agree to it, or have you conveniently forgotten that?'

Max suddenly sounded unutterably weary, Shauna thought, as he moved away. 'No, I haven't forgotten, and I have no intention of stopping you from seeing her. Just make sure that you telephone first, in future. I do not want you in my house when I'm not here.' A furrow appeared between the dark brows which framed his eyes. 'What is this, anyway? A lightning visit amid your social whirl? Passing through?'

Shauna couldn't miss the look of pleasure which appeared on Rupert's face.

'Sorry to disappoint you, dear boy—but I'm visiting my mother for Christmas. So we'll be neighbours again for a little while, at least.'

A muscle was working overtime in Max's cheek. 'How delightful,' he said sarcastically. 'And now, if you don't mind—I've had a very long day. You can see yourself out. You know the way.'

Rupert needed no second bidding. He picked up his jacket and slung it over his shoulder in record time, then turned and gave Shauna a smile which showed off every one of his dazzling white teeth. 'Nice to have met you. Pity to have broken up the party, but no doubt I'll be seeing you. Goodbye, Max—perhaps you could try suing the charm school!' He sauntered out of the room, and Shauna saw Max clenching his fists by his side.

They stood in silence until they heard the front door slam, heard the engine of his car revving up, scattering gravel as it roared away up the drive.

And suddenly all the fight seemed to go out of him. Shauna saw his hands relax; saw the tight muscular tension in his face replaced by a bleak, empty look which in its way was somehow more frightening than his anger.

She searched his face for a friendly sign, a sign that he was on her side, but there was none. He barely looked at her as he poured himself a large whisky, without offering her anything.

She curled a long strand of hair around her index finger in an unconsciously nervous movement. 'You don't seem to like him very much,' she said, stating the obvious and knowing how trite it sounded even as she said it.

He looked at her then, giving a short laugh before swallowing another mouthful of whisky. 'He's not my favourite person.'

She knew that she should feel irritated at his evasiveness, but she wasn't; instead she found herself in the invidious position of feeling guilty—and she didn't have a clue why. 'Why do you dislike him so much?' she asked. 'He seemed OK to me. A bit of a smoothie, perhaps, but harmless enough.'

She wished she hadn't asked, since she was rewarded with a chilly look. 'What goes on between Rupert and myself is of no concern to you, Shauna.'

Like a child wrongly accused of stealing, she found herself with the need to account for herself. 'He's been invited to a lot of balls this Christmas, and he needed someone to practise the waltz with, that's all . . .' Her words tailed off into an embarrassed silence, and she couldn't miss the faint curl of his lip.

'Really?' he mocked her. 'I had no idea that the waltz involved both partners grinding their pelvises together—but perhaps it's a new variation?'

She almost gasped aloud. The insult hit her like a pail of cold water. 'But it wasn't like that,' she protested, stung, and then she registered that his expression of disgust had intensified, and anger, a slow, insistent anger, began to build up inside her at the unjust criticism.

What God-given right did he have to talk to her in this way? Talk about double standards—*he* had just been off on what was obviously a sexual assignation with Marta, so what right did he have to come storming in here, just because he'd caught her dancing with a man?

'And what about *you*?' she taunted. 'Have you had a nice afternoon, Max?' She put on a sweetly sarcastic voice. 'How's dear Marta?'

Green eyes narrowed to shards of glass as he surveyed her. 'You don't know what you're talking about.' The voice was quiet, and controlled, but there was an underlying menace which warned off further questions.

She chose to ignore it. 'Oh, don't I? Well, I'm not *stupid*. Everyone knows what your relationship with Marta is, and, bearing that in mind—I doubt if you spent the day playing Scrabble with *her*, did you? I expect you had far more grown-up pursuits to follow!' She knew that her voice had a wild, high quality which bordered on hysteria, but she just couldn't stop the accusing words.

She saw anger darken his face, and his hands instinctively tighten into those tense fists again. And she saw by his face that she had gone much, much too far. She waited for the curt dismissal, the instruction to be gone in the morning, but he said nothing, simply stood regarding her with cold eyes.

Perhaps he was waiting for her to offer to go of her own volition—the self-imposed exile. She would have to suffer none of the ignominious treatment of being put out on the streets, jobless and homeless. That might rest a little too sharply on Max's conscience.

So she waited, and so did he. And she had proof then of just how much she did love him. For though he obviously wished her gone and regarded her, unjustly, as having the morals of an alley cat, she could stare back at him and still feel an implosion of desire which dominated every fibre of her being.

If, even with that expression of distaste, he had walked over to her then, and started to kiss her and touch her, and set her on fire with need—she would have let him. Let him take her to wherever he wanted, and make love to her.

And maybe that was what love was—desire, with the absence of all pride.

CHAPTER TEN

'I'VE dictated enough work to keep you occupied all day,' said Max coldly. 'I'll sign it when I get back. I'm taking Bianca out for the day.'

Shauna silently watched as he left the study. She had been dreading facing him after last night's awful confrontation with Rupert. She supposed she just ought to be grateful that he hadn't mentioned her outburst about Marta, she thought as she began typing. Or any of the rather sordid accusations they had each hurled at the other.

She found dinner that evening a difficult meal to endure, with only Bianca's chatter covering up both adults' lack of communication.

The days which followed were awful—with Max seeming to physically distance himself from her as much as possible. The work he left for her to do was demanding, and at any other time she would have welcomed the responsibility, but as it was—all she could think about was how much she missed his company.

Shauna was alone in the house one day when the telephone rang.

'Hello,' came a horribly familiar low voice.

'Hello?' replied Shauna, striving for a professionalism she was far from feeling.

'Is Max there?'

'No, I'm afraid he isn't. He's out with Bianca.'

'Oh.'

'Shall I . . . can I take a message?'

'Please. Just tell him that Marta rang, will you?'

'Yes, I'll tell him.' Shauna replaced the receiver slowly and sat staring at it for a long time.

'You've had a phone call,' she told him when he came in.

The green eyes surveyed her without emotion. 'Yes?'

'Marta rang.'

He nodded. 'Thanks.'

She felt a primitive urge to do him violence—to fling herself at him and pummel his chest with her fists, or something. Instead, she continued to type, like an automaton.

At dinner that night, Bianca turned to her. 'You will be here for Christmas, won't you, Shauna?'

Christmas was a subject she had deliberately pushed to the back of her mind. It always created something of a problem for her, with no family, but there were always friends to go to. But this year . . .

'I hadn't really thought about it,' she hedged.

'Oh, but you *must*, mustn't she, Dad?'

Max looked up. 'Shauna knows she's very welcome,' he said. 'It's entirely up to her. She may have friends she wishes to visit.'

Damn him, and his indifference, thought Shauna; why couldn't he just say stay, or go—give her some idea of whether or not he *did* want her there, instead of that chilly social mask he presented?

'Well, then,' smiled Bianca triumphantly. 'That's settled.'

And she was right of course, Shauna knew that. For where else would she have gone? And, more importantly, where else would she have wanted to go? Because however foolish she convinced herself it was—she *wanted* to spend Christmas with Max. And his indifference towards her didn't seem to alter that fact at all.

Two days before Christmas, they stopped work completely. At least, she thought thankfully, there was so much going on at Christmas that Bianca didn't seem to have picked up on the strained atmosphere between the two of them. She hoped.

Rupert visited to see his god-daughter, and Shauna was just returning from a brisk walk across the crisp, frozen grass of the December fields when she saw him getting into his car.

His handsome face lit up when he saw her, and he leaned against the car, one hand resting on his hip.

'So tell me, you rosy-cheeked beauty,' he said, without preamble. 'Are you coming to my party?'

It was impossible not to smile at his irrepressible flirting, she thought, glad that he hadn't brought up the scene of the other night. 'What party?'

He sighed. '*The* party, my dear. The party of the decade. People will kill to come to it—and the lady says to me "what party?" Chez Hamilton, on the twenty-sixth.'

She hastily did a mental calculation. Bianca was flying up to her grandparents in Scotland on Boxing

Day, and she and Max had planned to drive back to London.

She shook her head ruefully. 'I'll have gone by then. But thanks anyway.'

He affected a wounded expression. 'The gods most certainly do not love me! But if you change your mind... it starts at eight at Roakes House.'

She smiled. 'If I'm around—I wouldn't miss it for the world!'

He blew her a kiss and climbed into his car. He seemed in a hurry to get away, and she couldn't blame him. She stood for a moment watching the car drive away, lost in deep thought, and when she moved towards the door she started to find Max standing there, solid and dark, his stance both enticing and menacing as he watched her, faded denims stretching almost indecently across the firm muscular length of his legs, his dark features giving little away, and yet she couldn't mistake the flash of anger in his eyes as he watched Rupert's small sports car drive away.

She met his eyes defiantly. Perhaps he would like to have had written into her contract that she shouldn't converse with people of whom he didn't approve! He might have intimidated her into babbled explanations the other night, but he certainly wasn't going to get a repeat performance. 'Is anything the matter, Max?' she asked.

'What did he want?'

'Do you mean Rupert?' she asked, her voice all sweetness.

'You know I do,' he rasped.

She lifted her head high, so that the hood covering it slipped back to reveal the abundant cascade of jet-black curls, and she saw him step back a little, an unfathomable expression on the stern features. 'He was inviting me to a party he's having at his house.'

He scowled, looking astonishingly like his daughter. 'And are you going?'

Clear grey eyes met narrow green ones. Just what did he think he was playing at? *He* didn't want her, but he seemed far too concerned that somebody else might. Rupert didn't hold a candle to her boss as far as she was concerned, but she certainly wasn't going to give him the satisfaction of knowing that.

'I can't go,' she told him. 'Because it's on the twenty-sixth, and we're going back to town.' She saw him relax. 'Otherwise, I'd love to have gone,' she finished, and saw him glower again.

'Bianca's up in the attic, getting the tree decorations. She wanted . . . she wondered if you would help us decorate it?'

It had obviously cost him a huge effort to ask it, and it was patently not something that he particularly relished, and neither did she. There was something almost ridiculously intimate about dressing a Christmas tree, especially if it was with a man you'd fallen hopelessly in love with. She opened her mouth to decline the offer, but Bianca put paid to that, whirling out of the door like a dervish, yards of tinsel strewn around her neck like a dozen glittering scarves. She looked anxiously at Shauna, then back to her father.

'Did you ask her, Dad? Will you help us, Shauna? Oh, *please*?'

She looked down into the shining green eyes, so heart-catchingly like his, and smiled. 'Of course I'll help you. Where's the tree?'

'We'll have to go and choose it from the farm,' trilled Bianca excitedly. 'Won't we, Dad?'

Max looked as though someone had suggested a trip to the dentist, thought Shauna as she put her hood back up.

The three of them piled into the Range Rover, and Shauna surveyed the wintry landscape where the bare branches of the hedgerows which lined the lanes were so frosty that their tips looked as if they had been dipped in white paint.

They chose the biggest Christmas tree they could find and spent the afternoon decorating it.

Shauna was perched on the top of the ladder, when it wobbled precariously, and, as Max reached out to steady it, his hand brushed against her denim-clad thigh, and it was as though an electric shock had swept through her.

'That bolt needs tightening,' he muttered.

'Thanks.' Her voice was shaking, and it had nothing to do with an accident averted.

Her Christmas Day was actually much better than she'd anticipated, probably because they seemed to spend the entire day eating! She smilingly listened to Bianca's chatter as she unwrapped presents, and, if her laugh was brittle at times, she was sure that no one noticed it.

Bianca had bought her a whole array of matching combs, of every conceivable colour, and Max handed her a very large and very expensive bottle of perfume and, as she stammered her thanks, she found herself wondering what he had given to Marta. What a strange partnership they had. If she was his girlfriend, then why wasn't she here over Christmas?

By late afternoon, she was standing in front of the mirror in the dining-room. She had just finished pinning a strand of hair up with one of the combs Bianca had given her. It was black, and matched the clinging jersey dress. With most of her hair shimmering down her back, only the pale oval of her face showed against the blackness. She heard the softest of sounds and turned round to find Max silhouetted in the doorway, and she wondered how long he had been standing there.

The green eyes gave absolutely nothing away; at that moment he seemed nothing more than a polite stranger. 'Bianca's upstairs packing,' he said, sounding as if he'd chosen his words with care. 'Her flight's very early. I thought it would be best to start back to town as soon as possible after I get back.'

'Sure,' she nodded.

There was a long pause. Again she got the sensation of a rehearsed speech. The panacea for her disappointment that he hadn't made love to her.

'It hasn't been easy, this time here,' he said at last. 'I know that. But I want you also to know that I'm very grateful for everything you've done, especially for Bianca.' His mouth relaxed just a little. 'She's very fond of you, you know. Very fond.'

'I like her, too.'

'Yes, I know.' He cleared his throat. 'Can you be ready to leave as soon as I get back tomorrow morning, at around eleven?' There was another pause. 'I'm going off for a few days until the New Year. To the Cotswolds. I meet up with friends there every year. I'll drop you off in London first. It'll give us a break from one another—you can have the flat to yourself.'

But I don't need a break from you! she wanted to tell him, even while the cold stone of despair settled in the pit of her stomach as she tried to block out the picture of Marta—beautiful Marta—joining him. Because Cheltenham was in the Cotswolds, wasn't it? But none of these chaotic thoughts showed in her serene, frozen features. She was getting to be an accomplished actress, she reflected sadly.

'And when I get back—well, everything will be back to normal.'

'I hope so.' Whatever 'normal' was. Would anything ever be normal around this man?

The following day she waved farewell to a tearful, yet excited Bianca, amid promises to write. She felt a pang as the Range Rover tore off down the drive, with Max at the wheel. The reason for their close confinement was now gone and they would find it easier to avoid one another in town, but she would miss the elegant beauty of Seekings, the slow pace of rural community life. Even in these few short weeks Mrs Roberts had made her feel as though she belonged there. And let's face it, she thought, that was an all-time first.

Refusing to allow herself to become maudlin, she packed her cases and sat down with a coffee to wait for Max. She sat in her customary window-seat, enjoying her last few moments of the beautiful landscape outside, when a tableau began to develop before her as tiny flakes of snow started to fall—small scurries of them to begin with, then becoming great white blobs the size of coins, looking for all the world like a child's painting.

Within the hour the scene was transformed. Grass was now barely visible beneath the bright mantle. The leaden grey sky spilled the snow out relentlessly, and by twelve the whole landscape was covered by a thick, silent blanket.

By twelve. She started as she glanced again at her watch. Where on earth was Max? She strained her ears to listen for the deadened sound of the four-wheel drive as it bumped down the drive, but there was nothing.

She switched on the radio to hear the usual dire predictions by the weathermen, with warnings for no one to leave the house unless their journey was 'absolutely necessary'. Oh, Max, she thought. Just come home.

By three he still hadn't appeared or phoned and the light had started to fade. She was now seriously worried, imagining him stuck in drifts along some impassable country land, and was contemplating whether or not to ring the police to ask for advice when she heard his car draw up outside.

The door flew open and wind and snow blew in round him like a cloud, and she ran forward without thinking.

'Oh, Max,' she cried. 'Thank God you're back—I've been so worried.'

He took a step back, as if frightened she might hurl herself into his arms. 'I tried to call from the airport, but I think the lines are down. I would have tried again, but I didn't want to risk stopping.'

'Is Bianca all right?'

He nodded. 'The flight was delayed while they cleared the runway. I waited at the airport until news came in that they'd arrived in Scotland. By the time I started back the roads were already quite bad. I was lucky to get here at all. If I'd been in an ordinary car, I reckon I'd have been stuck there for the night.' There was a pause. 'This means, of course, that we shan't be able to get back to London, certainly not tonight.'

She bit her lip. 'Of course.' The big house seemed suddenly very silent. Bianca had gone away, and Mrs Roberts had long since left. They were cut off, isolated, marooned in a vast house which felt smaller by the second, and, by the look on his face, it was the last thing in the world he would have wished for.

'I'll go and shower. We'll eat in an hour.'

And in that instant she decided that what she was *not* going to do was to be told in that presumptuous way how she was going to spend the evening. She still had her pride, at least, and she was not going to scrabble around gratefully for the small crumbs of his company which he deigned to throw at her.

'Actually, I'm afraid you'll have to eat on your own,' she said coolly. 'I've been invited to a party.'

'Rupert's party?' he asked slowly.

'The very same.'

'You're not going to that.'

She didn't know whether he had intended it to come out as a flat command, but that was how it sounded and the way in which he said it filled her with anger. 'I *am* going,' she corrected.

'You'll never get down to the village in this weather—it's like Antarctica out there.'

'But that's not why you don't want me to go, is it, Max? This all has to do with Rupert, doesn't it?'

His voice was cold. 'He isn't your type.'

Her temper snapped. 'Oh, here we go again. You're full of advice, aren't you? What I want. What I don't want. How do you know what my "type" is? And I've made my mind up in any case— I'm going to the party whether you like it or not.'

'Then I'll drive you.'

'Oh, no, you won't,' she answered with icy dignity, but he had stepped forward and grabbed her by the upper arms, as if he were about to shake her.

'Oh, yes, I will,' he hissed. 'You can go to your damned party for all I care, but I'm not having you risking death to do so. What time do you want to leave?'

'At eight o'clock,' she blurted out, and ran upstairs to her room as fast as her feet could carry her, collapsing on the bed as soon as she'd slammed the door shut behind her, beating a helpless fist into the feather pillow, as if it were Max's chest she was hitting.

The harsh words had shaken her. She didn't understand him. Why *shouldn't* she go?

She spent hours getting ready since there was nothing else to do. Her hair took ages to dry properly, but it was worth it afterwards, for it shone like coils of ebony satin.

She had only one dress in her wardrobe which was suitable for a party such as Rupert's and that was one she had bought in Paris, en route to Portugal. It had been in a sale, naturally—a fantastic bargain, but she'd never had cause to wear it before.

Natural reticence made her hesitate a little before trying it on, but she gave a satisfied smile as she surveyed herself in the mirror. Daring, yes—but perfect.

In scarlet lace, it was outwardly demure with its high neck and long sleeves, but the buttoned bodice was fitted, emphasising the tiny waist, and the skirt lay snugly across her bottom, ending just above her knees and showing her long, black-stockinged legs. She would wear her wellingtons there, she decided, thinking about the snow—and change into the high-heeled black shoes when she arrived at Rupert's.

Like a complicated piece of fretwork, she began to pile the dark curls on to the top of her head, securing the whole lot in place with one linchpin of gold.

She darkened her eyelashes and applied scarlet lipstick to the wide lips more out of an act of defiance than anything else, though she wondered why she did it since the only man she was seeking to defy wouldn't even be at the party.

At just before eight, she was ready. Her wellies were down in the hall, she remembered, so she picked up her warm overcoat and, wrapping it around herself, she stepped out into the corridor.

Putting her shoes in her handbag, she tiptoed downstairs in her stockinged feet. She reached the bottom and saw that a fire had been lit in the study and standing, his back to her, was Max.

He must have heard her, for he turned slowly, his face forbidding, a glass of whisky in his hand. Without a word he slowly drank the contents of his glass then put the glass down on the mantelpiece and continued to stare at her, his hands resting on lean hips, an indecipherable expression on his face.

'I'm going out now,' she told him.

His eyes were skimming from the top of the elaborate hairstyle, down the all-concealing coat, to the slim ankles in their sheer stockings. 'So I see,' he grated.

She began to wish that she had insisted on walking, however great a folly that might have been. Well, she certainly wasn't going to *beg* him to take her. She gazed at him questioningly.

'And is the current fashion to go shoeless?' he enquired sarcastically.

'I'm going in my wellingtons—it *is* snowing,' she tried to smile.

It was as though something inside him had snapped. 'Damn you, Shauna!' he exploded. 'I don't want you to go!'

How dared he talk to her like that? 'So you told me!' She tossed her head in an age-old gesture of pique, causing the sensible coat to fall free of her grasp so that it flew open, and he was confronted with the sight of her in the clinging red dress.

He was staring at her, transfixed. 'I don't want you to go,' he repeated, and there was a low, husky quality to his voice.

'I'll bet you don't!' she retorted. 'And what alternative are you offering, perhaps you'd like to tell me that? A gloomy evening while you do your best to avoid me? You don't want me, do you, Max? And yet you can't bear the thought that someone else might!'

She heard a long sigh, like the hissing of steam, escape from the hard line of his mouth.

The air was tight with tension as he stared at her incredulously. 'Not want you?' He closed the gap between them with one purposeful step. 'Not want you,' he repeated. 'Oh, really, Shauna?' The green eyes glittered. 'Come here,' he whispered. 'Come here and feel how much I don't want you.' And in a swift, decisive movement, his hand snaked round her waist, pulling her hard towards him, so that she was moulded against the full length of his body, but, as if that weren't enough, he pushed his hips into hers so that they fitted together, like two parts of a puzzle. 'You see?' he bent and murmured softly in her ear. 'How much?'

It was the most deliberately wanton and explicit thing that had ever happened to her. Every nerve-ending was tingling with awareness. They had been close before, but never this close. The hardness of him jutting against her soft curves. Yes, she could feel his desire for her. Oh, God. She closed her eyes.

It was glaringly apparent—even through the thick denim of his jeans.

His mouth came down on hers, hard, but it met no resistance. He tipped her head back as his tongue probed intimately and she closed her eyes in delirious pleasure as his hand began to move slowly across her back, against the crisp lace of the dress which suddenly seemed an encumbrance.

The blood was singing and rushing through her veins, her heart beating out loudly and insistently like a primitive drum, when the voice of reason began clamouring to be heard.

Every one of her senses began screaming its protest as she pulled her lips away from him, as she tried ineffectually to push at the hard muscle of his chest, her fist balled against the frantic hammering of his own heart.

The green eyes looked almost opaque with desire, their pupils huge, dark shutters. 'What are you doing?' he groaned, pulling her back into his arms, but she kept her head averted, and pulled away. 'Shauna, what is it?'

She forced her ragged breathing to acquire some semblance of normality as she surveyed him. 'I thought this was what you most emphatically didn't want? Wasn't it you who told me "no more"?'

He shook his head. 'I just can't fight it any more. I want you, Shauna.'

Her eyebrows shot up at the arrogant ease of reply. 'Just like that?' Her voice rang out. 'You've changed your mind? You can pick me up or put me down whenever the fancy takes you? Well, I'm sorry, Max—it won't work. Not with me. I'm not prepared to be your substitute. No one likes to be made love to knowing that they're just filling in for someone else.'

'What the hell are you talking about?'

The pain of being separated from him when her body was crying out for fulfilment made the timbre of her voice unusually brittle. 'You know damn well what I'm talking about! Shall I put it into plain English for you? You need a woman! And you're using me because I happen to be around—because Marta isn't here!'

CHAPTER ELEVEN

MAX'S voice was ominously quiet. 'What did you say?'

'You heard exactly what I said.'

His face was all dark planes and shadows. 'You don't know what you're talking about.'

The bitterness of the last few days came spilling out. 'Oh, don't I? You aren't denying, are you, Max, that Marta is your mistress?'

'We had,' he said softly, 'an understanding.'

Shauna recoiled. So he didn't even try to deny it. She shut her eyes as if by doing that she could shut out the thoughts which tortured her. When she opened them again, she stared at him—fury darkening the grey eyes. 'Why aren't you with *her*, then? Why don't you go to her, make love to her, and stop using me as a substitute?'

'Stop talking like that!' he yelled.

'Why? Does the truth hurt?' she yelled back. 'Tell me, is Marta busy tonight? Or is it because of the weather? I suppose that if you weren't actually snowed in here with me then you wouldn't have to resort to sex with me!'

'Stop it,' he grated. 'You don't usually talk this way.'

'Well, these aren't exactly usual circumstances, are they?' she asked, sweetly sarcastic. 'And you're not denying, are you, Max, that our—en-

tanglement the other night left you feeling more
than a little frustrated? So at the first opportunity
you rush off to Marta—who can give you what you
didn't seem to want from me?'

He pulled her back into his arms then, and the
jarring shock of the renewed close proximity sent
her senses reeling, so that she found resistance impossible. 'I'll tell you what happened, shall I,
Shauna, if you really want to know? Yes, I had
planned to go to Marta that night. Because, yes, I
thought that there was only one sure-fire way to get
you out of my system . . .' His eyes had become
hooded, cautious.

'Marta and I have known one another for a long
time. We're both adults. No ties. No questions. The
only kind of relationship which suits me. An easy
understanding which suited us *both*. Until now.
Yes, you stirred me up that night. I won't deny that
I wanted you in a way that I haven't wanted a
woman for a long time. But you work with me.
You share a flat with me. An affair would com-
plicate that—and I'm not looking for a partner.
And so I intended to go to Marta.' His eyes gave
nothing away. 'But it was . . . no good.'

'I don't understand,' she said coldly. If he had
taken a blunt, heavy instrument and smashed her
over the head with it, he could not have hurt her
more.

'Do you want me to spell it out in words of one
syllable?' he said bitterly. 'I didn't even get there—
I just drove around for hours and hours, my head
in a spin. I couldn't have gone to bed with Marta
that night, nor anyone else for that matter. Because

some dark-haired witchy woman had got underneath my skin, had got into my blood, and I didn't
want anyone but her.'

She stared at him stupidly. 'What are you
saying?'

'That I want you, Shauna. *You*. Very much.'

But he was saying it as though he was still fighting
it, she thought desperately, even while his eyes were
devouring her. There was a muscle working
overtime in his cheek; she could see a pulse hammering under the smooth brown skin of his temple.

And suddenly she knew that she wanted no
turning back, not any more. She loved him. She
wanted him too much. If she let this moment go,
she might never have another like it, with the
promise of everything she knew that he would give
her. She didn't care whether it was right or wrong.
She wanted this man, but it went deeper than that.
Desire, yes—but there was need, too. Real need.
There was an empty space in her mind and body
and soul. A space that only he could fill. A flickering flame just waiting to grow into a glowing
blaze, a flame which he had ignited and only he
could extinguish. She wanted him—and to hell with
the consequences. She would never be able to work
for him again after tonight, in any case.

His eyes were riveted to the heaving movement
of her breasts. He stood as if carved from stone—
silent and unmoving. Now, she thought. Now.

Very deliberately, she raised her hand to remove
the glittering golden pin and it fell to the ground
with a little clatter as the mass of dark curls tumbled
down around her shoulders like a mantilla. She let

her heavy coat slither to the floor, and as she did so she saw him start.

'Shauna...' he said unsteadily.

She had not finished. Slowly, she started to undo each of the tiny, covered buttons of the bodice.

He was watching her, mesmerised.

She took her time. She could hear his ragged, uncontrollable breathing puncturing the silence as her fingers slowly released button after button. The final one free, she smiled, her eyes widening with pleasure at the look on his face as she peeled the bodice right down, revealing the lush honey-coloured breasts, with their rose-dark nipples.

And it was as though someone had breathed sudden life into him. His eyes darkened. He beckoned very slowly. 'Now come here,' he whispered.

She went, willingly, her arms automatically going around his neck, while he grasped the slender nakedness of her waist.

He groaned as he buried his face in her hair, his hands moving to cup and caress each breast, his mouth starting out on a moist, sensual path from neck to mouth, so that when he finally crushed her mouth with his lips she returned the kiss with a feverish intensity which equalled his.

With one fluid movement he slipped the dress down over her hips and then effortlessly lifted her high in the air, so that she was free of it and left wearing nothing but her lace panties and black stockings.

Still kissing her, he pushed her down on to the softness of the Persian rug, and leaned over her, his hand lightly circling each breast in turn, so that she made a tiny cry at the back of her throat.

He heard it and bent his head to her ear. 'You,' he whispered, 'are very beautiful. And I am feeling slightly over-dressed.'

'Oh, Max.' Her voice sounded thick and slurred. Her nipples felt bruised and hard as they brushed against his shirt. She tightened her arms around his neck, but felt him removing them and she opened her eyes, terrified that he was going to stop.

He must have read the question in her eyes. 'Oh, no,' he murmured. 'I'm not going anywhere.' And he stood up, his eyes never leaving her face as he slowly began to unbutton his shirt. He pulled the shirt off and threw it aside, revealing the magnificent torso she'd seen that first night in the flat, the smooth brown skin sheathing the rippling muscle beneath.

She lay, arms above her head, watching his every move. His eyes travelled over every inch of her, lingering on her breasts until she felt them tingle and throb, their tips jutting towards him in tight twin erections, as if he were touching them instead of just looking at them. His gaze moved down to the tiny flimsy wisp of her panties, the little lacy suspender belt, and the black stockings which clung to her long legs.

His hand lingered on the button of his jeans. 'How far do you want me to go?' he grinned.

'Everything.' Her husky reply was barely audible. She started to tremble as he slid the zip down with a tantalising lack of speed. The jeans came off slowly, inch by inch, until he stood in front of her, gloriously proud in his nakedness.

Her pupils dilated as she saw how aroused he was, and without realising it she licked her bruised lips and he saw it, and the game suddenly stopped and he was lying on top of her, his eyes dark with passion, and she felt his need pushing insistently against her stomach.

He traced a lazy line from stomach to thigh, a finger moving to find the moist scrap of her panties, and she gave a stifled moan.

'Now these,' he whispered, as he slid them down past her knees, 'I think we'll dispense with. But these . . .' his hand rested on a silk-stockinged thigh, 'I think we'll leave on, shall we?'

She was past caring, or answering—he had her in such a feverish state of wanting that she felt she would explode soon. She moved ecstatically as his fingers explored the soft, satiny centre of her that cried out for his possession. And it seemed that he knew she could wait no longer, for he thrust into her powerfully, without warning, filling her totally with himself. She astonished herself with her own frantic movements, wrapping her silk-clad thighs around his back, capturing him—when, as if answering an unspoken need, he drove into her harder until, with a sharp cry that was torn from her lips, she fell over the top, spinning out of control, aware then of spasm after glorious spasm pulsating around his hardness. And when he cried out too, she enfolded him fiercely against her breasts, their bodies joined, the waves ebbing and dying in unison—bringing utter contentment, and peace.

She awoke to find him watching her and he made slow love to her all over again, and, later in the night, when the fire had died, he carried her up to his room and laid her on the bed.

He knelt over her, his eyes skimming her from head to foot, as if he had a need to memorise every inch of her. He ran both his hands down over the contours of her body, moulding them briefly to her breasts, and down, over her stomach, over her thighs, resting at last on her ankles, still in their black stockings.

'I think these can come off now,' he murmured. 'Mmm?'

'Anything you like,' she said throatily, and he laughed delightedly.

'Oh, sweetheart—you don't know what you've just let yourself in for,' he teased.

'I do. . .' Her drowsy words faded as the insistent pleasure began to build up again.

His hand moved slowly up her leg, so slowly that it was sweet torture, and she waited breathlessly, letting out a tortured little cry as he halted at her stocking top, a forefinger moving within the lacy rim, before unclipping it and slowly sliding it off.

When he had each leg bare, he began to kiss her toes, then her ankles, her knees and the inside of her thighs. And then his mouth found the velvety core, moving so intimately against her that she felt a brief moment of stunned shock before the slow heat took over and she could scarcely believe when it happened again, her delirious cry sounding loud in the stillness of the night. She was still shuddering uncontrollably when her hands reached down for him blindly until she had located the broad bank of his shoulders and he moved to lie above her, laughing a little as he bent his head to kiss her.

'Shauna...' he groaned. 'Oh, God. Feel. Feel what you're doing to me.' And he pulled her even closer.

She felt the hardness of him, the throbbing power of his arousal which filled her with a sense of wonder that he wanted her again so badly, and so soon.

She awoke slowly the next morning, naked and glowing beneath the rumpled sheets, and it took a few seconds for her to register that he was no longer beside her.

She stretched luxuriously, her long arms moving uninhibitedly above her head, frozen in an indolent pose. Part of the sheet slipped to reveal a naked brown thigh, and she buried her face in his pillow as she re-lived the memories of the previous night, moment by glorious moment.

It had been indescribable, and Max, as a lover, quite perfect. There had been only one other man in her life, and that had been Harry. He had been serious. She had *thought* she was serious. After the kind of deliberations which had never even entered her head with Max, she had gone to bed with him, and the sex had served to diminish, rather than enhance the relationship. They had agreed to part as friends shortly after.

But with Max—it had been something else. He had made love to her almost all night long—she hadn't thought that possible. He had done things to her which should have made her blush, and yet she was filled with impatient longing to have him do them to her all over again. He had slept briefly with her held tightly in his arms, and she had drifted in and out of a dazed slumber, filled with happiness every time she opened her eyes to find her gorgeous, naked Max beside her. And now, without him, she felt as though she'd lost a part of herself. Where was he?

She sat up, taking in the surroundings which last night had gone ignored. It was an overwhelmingly masculine room with dark crimson walls and framed sporting prints predominating. Through the open door of his wardrobe she could see piles of expensive-looking sweaters stacked.

This was a room where a woman would only have one place, and she was in it. All of a sudden, she felt like an intruder, and she pushed the sheets aside and padded over to the door to where a towelling robe of Max's hung. She put it on and pulled the belt tightly around her waist, ran her fingers through her curls to untangle them a little, and went off in search of him.

In the mirror in the hallway, she caught sight of a sparkling-eyed girl with pink cheeks flushed with happiness. That's me! she thought in delight.

She could hear noises coming from the kitchen, and she moved lightly towards it.

As she was barefooted, he hadn't heard her. He had his back to her and was filling the percolator. She looked at him adoringly, at the broad shoulders and the long, clean line of his limbs. At the way the dark hair curled on to his neck.

He was wearing jeans and a sweater, and a feeling of regret filled her. She would have much preferred to forgo the coffee and have him wake up naked next to her.

'Hello, you,' she whispered softly, and he turned round, his face carefully composed, not looking like Max at all.

'Good morning,' he said. 'Would you like some coffee?'

'Love some,' she lied, her heart thudding with fear. She didn't want coffee, she wanted him to come over to her and kiss her, and tell her she was beautiful, and rid her of the insecurity which had suddenly threatened to overwhelm her. Instead of which, he was looking at her as if she were a stranger, with that horrible polite little smile on his face.

He handed her the cup, but her hand was shaking so much that it danced wildly in the saucer, shattering the silence with its clinking clamour. She put it down on the work surface quickly.

All at once she felt totally unsure of herself, remembering that she had been the seducer last night. It had been her act—her flagrant and provocative strip-tease—which had pushed him over the edge— beyond reason and into her arms. If today he was regretting what had happened, she had only herself to blame.

Suddenly, she could bear it no longer. 'Max, you're regretting last night, aren't you? Wishing that it had never happened?'

There was a long pause. When he looked up, his eyes were guarded. 'I don't think that now is a very good time to talk,' he said abruptly. 'Drink your coffee—and then you'd better get dressed. I have to drop you back in London, before I leave for the Cotswolds.'

She stared at him as if he had just uttered the most foul obscenity. 'Cotswolds?' she echoed foolishly.

'Yes. It's a long-standing arrangement. You knew that.'

Yes, she had known. But she had thought— what? That last night had changed things? And why should it have done? What had he said to indicate that it might be otherwise? Nothing. Absolutely nothing. He had taken her to bed, and she had *known* that part of him was unwilling to. But what kind of man could resist that kind of temptation? It must have been the most unsubtle come-on since time began.

She felt her cheeks grow hot, and, afraid that she might suddenly start to cry, she turned away rapidly, blinking back the tears.

'I'll go and get dressed,' she said in a calm voice that seemed to come from a long way away.

'I'll wait here.'

He obviously wanted to be nowhere near her.

All the while she was getting ready, she had to fight to suppress the mental images which were crowding her mind with sickening clarity. Of Max—doing all those things to Marta that he had done to her, last night.

True, he had said that he couldn't have gone to bed with Marta or 'anyone else for that matter', because his thoughts had been full of Shauna. But that was before he'd taken her to bed, and, presumably, he had now got her out of his system, leaving him free to return to Marta once more. He had certainly acted as though he had got her out of his system. Why, he had scarcely been able to be civil to her this morning. He hadn't spoken more than a few words to her.

She sank on to the bed, her head in her hands, shoulders shaking convulsively. What did she expect, when she'd behaved like a cheap little tramp?

The journey back was worse than atrocious. The roads were still fairly treacherous, and Max needed every bit of his wits to keep the Range Rover on the road, and out of the drifts on either side.

But even taking into account the conditions, there could be no denying that an awkward silence had invaded the car when their journey started, and it was multiplying by the moment.

The silence grew so lengthy and so brittle that it became impossible to break. For what would they have said? What could they have said, given the circumstances?

For how pitiful it would have been to have heard their dramatically opposing views, from Shauna's 'I love you, Max', to his 'thanks, but no thanks'.

She was glad when they hit London, even though she knew that the sooner they arrived, the sooner he would be gone.

In the flat she heard him moving around in his room. She stood, feeling totally alone as she stared sightlessly out at the panoramic view.

She heard his footfall behind, but she stayed unmoving.

'Shauna?'

Feeling empowered to face him, she turned, but any hope of a change of heart died instantly on seeing his face. It was as coolly indifferent as it had been all morning.

'I have to go now.'

'Yes.' She was astonished how normal her response sounded.

'I'll see you when I get back. We'll talk then.'

'Yes, Max.' It was an automatic reply. She scarcely registered what he was saying.

'Goodbye.' He hesitated as if to say something more, but evidently changed his mind, for then he turned on his heel and left, without uttering another word.

CHAPTER TWELVE

ONCE Max had gone, Shauna allowed herself the luxury of tears. She lay on her bed like an emotional teenager, and howled. By the time she'd finished she had a blotchy face, shiny nose, and was sniffing like someone with severe adenoidal problems. And still didn't feel any better.

She took a shower—there hadn't been time at Seekings. Max still clung to her skin; the masculine scent of him seemed to surround her, and she was strangely reluctant to wash it away.

And even when she was clean, she still ached, and was tender—there were several small bruises where he'd delectably bitten and sucked at her skin. It was as though she would never be able to rid herself of him.

With hair dripping like seaweed, she made some coffee and sat down to think.

Wouldn't it just be best if she left while he was away? Threw herself on the mercy of Harry and Nick, and stayed with them until she found somewhere of her own?

But wouldn't that be the cowardly way out? Running away had never solved anything. If there was to be nothing between them, then surely it would be better if she faced up to it. Max had said that they would talk when he returned. About what? About what a wonderful time he'd had in the Cotswolds with Marta?

She clenched her fist very tight and pressed it to her lips. What had she expected? Wedding bells? Max had been quite straightforward about the relationship he had with Marta—'the only type of relationship which suits me'. And yes, he had desired Shauna enough to stop him from visiting Marta that night, but now his desire had been satiated, and, in going to bed with him, surely Shauna had lost her elusiveness, and her desirability. For a man like Max would be so used to getting just what he wanted from any woman that surely to remain immune to his charm would be the only way of guaranteeing any degree of respect from him.

She had thrown herself at him. He had been fighting the attraction, but she had stood in front of him and stripped to the waist in an attempt to seduce him.

And the next day, what had happened? He had leapt out of bed and distanced himself from her as much as was humanly possible. He had driven her back to town, as hastily as possible, and had left her for a pre-planned holiday with the woman he had shared his life with for goodness only knew how long.

Perhaps in the sophisticated world these people inhabited this kind of liaison was par for the course. Perhaps Marta understood and forgave Max his little 'indiscretions'. The fist pressed tighter against her mouth, as she fought to control the tears.

Yet, still, she hoped. She didn't contact either Harry or Nick. Instead she hung around the flat, hoping against hope that Max might ring her. But he didn't. Not the first night, or the second either.

By the third, she was feeling like a caged lioness with the sentence of death hanging over her head, when there was a loud ring at the door. She jumped to her feet, and spoke into it breathlessly.

'Hello?'

It was Charlie, the commissionaire. 'There's a gentleman down here to see you, Miss Wilde,' he said.

Even though logic told her that Max certainly wouldn't have announced his presence through Charlie, still she hoped. 'Who is it, Charlie?'

'It's a Mr Hamilton.'

Rupert! If she hadn't been preparing to go to Rupert's party the other night, then the whole bed bit with Max might never have happened. And yet she found herself wanting to see him, hoping that his flippant sense of humour might rock her out of the doom-laden mood which was enveloping her. She cleared her throat. 'That's all right, Charlie,' she told him. 'You can send him up.'

Rupert rapped on the door seconds later. 'Hello, beauty,' he said without preamble, then looked at her more closely, and his eyes widened. 'Or should I say—the beast? What have you been doing to yourself? You look dreadful!'

There was no way she was going to tell him, telling would only make her think about it, and she was sick to death of thinking about and analysing the whole sorry affair. 'Lack of sleep, combined with a heavy cold,' she muttered, which was half true. 'What are you doing here?'

He grinned. 'I pursued you! There's nothing I find quite so attractive as a woman who plays hard to get. I thought you'd come to my party—I really did. So when you didn't I decided to come calling.'

'Oh,' she said listlessly. Flirting was right at the bottom of her list of priorities today.

He frowned a little, and sat down on one of the sofas, spreading his legs before him elegantly, and threading his fingers together before his chest in an almost prayer-like attitude. 'Where's Max?'

A hammer pounded at her chest. 'In the Cotswolds.'

'Ah, yes—his yearly ritual. I hear that the luscious Marta is moving into the big-time. Apparently she's landed *Vogue*, and *Elle*.'

The hammer became heavier. Rupert had made the connection that Marta would be there, too. She found herself looking helplessly at him.

'So you're free tonight?' he smiled. 'No evil boss standing over you as your fingers whizz over the word processor?'

She managed a wan smile. 'No.'

'Good!' He grinned. 'Want to come to a party with me?'

Did she? She hesitated. Why not? she thought defiantly. Why mope around, waiting for a phone-call which patently wasn't going to come, while Max wined and dined Marta in the Cotswolds? Why *should* she stay at home? In truth, she could have done with a long bath, a glass of wine, and a full night's sleep. But sleep was at a premium lately, and she'd probably spend the night tossing and turning. There was a sense of retaliation in her reply. 'Thank you, Rupert—I'd love to come out with you.' Anything Max could do, she could do better.

Rupert looked her up and down. 'You're going to need a bit of time to cover up those bags underneath your eyes—so get cracking!'

An hour later, Shauna emerged from her bedroom wearing the scarlet lace dress. As she'd slowly buttoned it up, she had had to close her mind firmly to the vivid memories of Max pushing the gown to the floor, Max pulling her naked into his arms... Those thoughts were nothing but self-destructive.

She'd left her hair loose, and it snaked down her back in a froth of jet curls. As she appeared, Rupert gave an appreciative whistle. *'Unbelievable,'* he murmured.

The party was in Chelsea, and was rowdy, noisy and reeking of far too much money. There were a lot of people called Sophie and Henrietta and once Rupert called 'James' across the room, and at least eight people turned round.

There were bottles of warm champagne everywhere, and Shauna found herself sipping some out of a silver christening mug, listening while Rupert and another man argued fiercely over whether the property market would ever recover.

At eleven, they all convened to 'Lulu's' nightclub, where the party continued.

From time to time, Rupert would give Shauna a comforting squeeze on the shoulder. 'Enjoying yourself?' he queried.

'Mmm!' Another sip of the tepid fizz. Was she enjoying herself? Not really. But it was a damn sight better than being back at the flat, feeling sorry for herself.

The music changed down to slow and smoochy, and Rupert took Shauna into his arms. The wine she had drunk had made her feel just nicely mellow, and properly relaxed for the first time since Max had driven her back. He bent his head to whisper, 'Having fun?'

And strangely enough, considering the circumstances, she was—simple, uncomplicated fun, with a simple, uncomplicated man. 'Yes,' she nodded. 'I am.'

He immediately tightened his hold and began to rub his hand down the back of her neck, but Shauna stiffened and he must have felt it, for he stepped back a little, and looked at her questioningly. 'No?'

She shook her head ruefully. 'No. But no offence?'

He shrugged easily. 'None taken.'

What a wonderfully uncomplex man, she thought sadly. Why couldn't she fall for someone like Rupert?

At two o'clock, they began to gather up their belongings, smiling as they made their way through the crush. Rupert had his arm tightly around Shauna's waist to guide her through the crowd, and, when they pushed their way out into the night, there was a shout, and a blinding flash, which startled Shauna, causing her to fall back against him.

She blinked in confusion as Rupert bundled her into a cab. 'What was that?'

'The bloody Press,' he told her. 'They prowl around like vultures.'

But Shauna thought he didn't look displeased.

Perhaps due to the wine and the dancing, she slept deeply, not waking up, amazingly, until almost ten-thirty, then lay there until eleven, knowing that, pride or no pride, she would wait for however long it took for Max to come back, to hear what it was he wanted to say to her.

She dressed in jeans and an old sweater and was just stifling a yawn when she heard a key in the door and in walked Max. Marta went straight out of her head and her first instinct was to hurl herself eagerly into his arms, but something in his face stopped her.

'Max . . . ?' she said diffidently.

'Feeling tired, are we?' he asked, thinly veiled contempt in his voice.

Her eager expression became wooden as she stared into his cold, indifferent face. She had hoped against hope that he would still want her, but she had been wrong. There could be only one reason for this harsh, frightening Max. He wanted her out of his life. She struggled to say something which would not have her pride in tattered shreds in front of him.

'Did—did you have a good time?' she stammered, her voice dangerously close to tears.

At the gauche question, something inside him seemed to snap and he grabbed her shoulders with a force which made her wince with pain.

'How could you?' he spat out. 'Couldn't you even wait for a few meagre days?'

She shrank away from the blazing venom in his eyes. His grip on her was like a vice. 'You—you're hurting me,' she said weakly.

He didn't relinquish his hold on her at all. 'Hurting you? Believe me, Shauna, I'm using every bit of restraint in my body at this moment. I'd like to kill you,' he hissed. 'Or perhaps I know a better way to get to you. Shall I turn you on? And then leave you? Leave you wanting me? Hmm? Shall I do that? Would you like that, Shauna?' he whispered. 'Would you like me to...?' The words he used were not loving words. He pulled her into his arms and pressed her close to him, and, even while she recoiled from the violence in his tone, her body reacted involuntarily to the movement. He must have felt it, too, for she saw her self-disgust mirrored in his eyes, and he dropped his hands immediately, as if she were a piece of old garbage he could not bear to touch.

Sanity fought to make itself heard. Even if he had decided that he no longer wanted anything to do with her, that did not account for this—this seeming hatred of her.

'What is it, Max?' she croaked, from terror-dried lips. 'What is it?'

'What is it?' he mimicked tauntingly. 'As if you didn't know. And who did you have lined up for tonight? Rupert again? Or someone else?' He stared at her consideringly. 'I must say, you had even *me* fooled with your enthusiastic once-in-a-lifetime response—quite the little actress, aren't you?'

She prayed that none of this was happening to her, that she was in the midst of some diabolical nightmare. 'I don't know what you're talking about,' she muttered wearily.

'Then maybe this will help,' he said, with icy disdain. He pulled out a newspaper from the inside pocket of his jacket. It was one of the popular tabloids. It fell open at the gossip column, and there, coming out of the nightclub, was a picture of Shauna and Rupert.

It had never occurred to her that they might use it—true, Rupert was a minor aristocrat, but she, Shauna, was of no consequence.

She looked more closely at the photograph. As a piece of evidence it was about as damning as you could get. They said the camera didn't lie, but in this case they'd got it wrong, for it looked like a photograph of a couple who couldn't keep their hands off each other. Like lovers.

It was all there to see. Rupert's hand clasped tightly and protectively around her waist. Her flushed and shining face frozen in a smile as the long tendrils of her hair splayed all over his white shirt-front where she leaned against him.

She looked up to find the green eyes surveying her coldly. She made one last, desperate bid. 'It wasn't like that!' she cried, knowing the futility of the words even as she uttered them.

'Oh, sure,' he ground out harshly. 'And there's gold at the end of the rainbow.'

He wasn't even giving her a chance, she realised, and stared at him then, recognising an irrefutable truth. That in a way he had wanted this. He wasn't looking for a partner, he had told her that, and now here she was, handing to him on a plate the perfect excuse to reject her.

Her words of denial died on her lips. What was the point of begging him, pleading with him to believe her? Why humiliate herself further? He seemed to have one rule for himself, and another for her. *He* could go tripping off with Marta, and yet he had blown a fuse at a stupid little photograph in a down-market rag, without even bothering to validate it.

He didn't want to believe her. He wanted to find her guilty, and, in so doing, that allowed him to reinforce all his prejudices against women. Only he could destroy those prejudices, and he simply didn't want to.

Even if she could convince him that in this case the picture told the wrong story, would he ever truly believe her, or trust her? There was no trust left in Max's heart—that was a truth she had hit on weeks ago—and to live without trust would not be living at all.

'I want you out of here,' he said in a flatly controlled voice, before he turned away and walked towards the door.

'Oh, don't worry, Max—I'm out of here. Nothing in the world would make me stay!' she called at his retreating back, wanting him to hear that her own voice was controlled too, in a last wild attempt to hang on to an appearance of dignity.

But she wasn't even sure that he could hear her, and the last thing she saw was the line of his broad shoulders, now hopelessly distorted as she viewed them through a veil of tears.

CHAPTER THIRTEEN

LIFE in the flat was cramped. Very cramped. Naturally, Shauna was glad to have a roof over her head, and grateful to Harry and Nick for taking her in so suddenly, and without question. And questions must have been swarming around in their minds that morning, when she had turned up with her suitcase, not crying, but clearly in a terrible state.

And she decided fairly quickly that two and a half years on down the line she had changed the way she liked to live. She had tolerated the mess at twenty-one, but now she preferred a calmer, more ordered life.

Each morning, when she opened her eyes to the unwashed dishes, the overflowing ashtrays, shoes kicked hither and thither, she heaved a great sigh and tried to put all comparisons with Seekings out of her mind.

She couldn't really close her eyes to the mess, either, since she was sleeping in the sitting-room. There were only two bedrooms—Harry had the smaller one, and Nick shared his with Heather, his girlfriend. Consequently, Shauna had to wait up until everyone else was ready to go to bed, or 'crash', as they insisted on putting it, the smell of wine and smoke making her feel nauseated. Harry, in the meantime, kept making jocular suggestions that she share his room, and, although he was light-hearted about it, she knew that he would have been delighted if she *had* taken him up on his offer. Because of this, Shauna no longer felt as relaxed in Harry's company as she used to, afraid that any great show of friendship might be misinterpreted.

She quickly found herself a temping job. It was about as menial as you could get—invoice typing in an airless office with two other girls—but at least it didn't require any brainwork—her mind felt totally numb, and she wasn't sure that she could have coped with anything more demanding. And at least it paid her contribution towards the rent.

In her spare time, she went flat-hunting, gloomily looking over dingy and over-priced lodgings which all seemed to share two distinct characteristics— they all smelt, and the bathrooms should have carried a public health warning.

On the subject of Max, she did not dwell at all. Thoughts of Max were taboo, they led nowhere, and, besides, other thoughts had now blocked out *all* thoughts of Max because the last couple of mornings had brought about a very real fear indeed...

One Wednesday evening, almost three weeks after she'd left Max's flat, there was a loud rat-ta-tat on the door. She stirred a little in the armchair. Keeping very still seemed to make the sickness retreat a little. But Harry and Nick and Heather were all out, so she'd have to answer it. Not that it was likely to be for her—no one knew where she was living. Apart from Max—and *he* wouldn't come.

It was Rupert. He frowned when he saw her. 'You look even worse than last time I saw you!' he exclaimed.

'Thanks a bunch.' But she couldn't be cross with him for long. His voice held no malice, only concern. 'How did you know where I was living?'

'Max.'

Her heart raced. 'What did he say?'

Rupert shook his head. 'I didn't actually speak to him. His new secretary gave me your address.'

His new secretary. 'He's replaced me, then,' she said in a small, resigned voice. In his office, and in his bed.

Rupert was looking at her closely. 'Are you OK, Shauna? Can I come in?'

She nodded. 'Sure.' She saw his nose wrinkle a little as he stepped inside. She'd cleaned the sitting-room, but Buckingham Palace it wasn't. Well, it was too bad.

To her surprise, his face held an unusually gentle look. 'Shauna, what in hell's name are you doing here?'

Grey eyes were turned moodily in his direction. 'What does it look like? I'm living here.'

'But why? It's dreadfully small.'

It was proving impossible to stop her voice from trembling. 'Because I had nowhere else to go, that's why!'

'But you were happy at Max's, weren't you?'

She turned on him; she knew that it wasn't his fault, but she couldn't help herself. 'Yes, I was very happy at Max's, but he thinks...thinks...' Her voice faded away into a whisper.

'Thinks what?'

Her grey eyes glittered with unshed tears. 'He thinks that I'm having an affair with you.'

He shook his head in disbelief. 'No, he can't. Why should he think that?'

'Because of the photo, of course!' she cried.

'The photo?'

'In the paper! In the wretched gossip column!'

Rupert stood up abruptly, and stared at her. 'He thought that?' he said slowly, then nodded his head, as if in confirmation of his own question. 'Yes, he would,' he said, almost as an afterthought. The bright blue eyes were questioning. 'And tell me something, Shauna. How do you feel about Max?'

She shook her head. 'It doesn't matter any more. It's too late.'

'No!' All at once, his voice sounded very adult and serious as he read the answer in her eyes. 'It's not too late. It's never too late, Shauna. Only death makes things too late...'

Shauna frowned as she saw pain shutter the usually carefree face, and, moments later, it was as if he had been galvanised into action, for he moved quickly towards the door.

'Aren't you going to stay—for tea, or something?' she asked, thinking as she did so how tired her voice sounded.

'Things to do,' he said briskly, and shut the door behind him.

Harry and Nick still hadn't returned, and Shauna had been sick twice, when the door went again. She sighed as she got up to open it, then almost crumpled when she saw who it was who stood there, dripping wet, as though he had been standing in the rain for a long time.

She stared at him, white-faced. 'What are you doing here, Max?'

'May I come in?'

She hesitated. What good could come from seeing him?

The green eyes narrowed. 'Please?'

She nodded, afraid to speak, and opened the door for him.

He bent his head a little as he stepped inside. The flat, which was small anyway, immediately shrank to doll's-house-like proportions. He seemed almost larger than life—she'd forgotten the glowing vibrancy which he gave off as an aura.

She had expected to feel a mass of confused emotions. What she had not expected was to find that she felt exactly the same about him. There was still that warm rush of longing, still the desire to be encircled in those strong, protective arms. Her body still knew a sharpening reaction to his proximity. He had broken her heart and she was fickle enough to love him still.

They faced one another across the shabby hearthrug. She thought that even in a few weeks he looked different. Thinner, with skin stretched tight over a face which was rigid with tension. And she knew that she looked different, too. Pale-faced and hollow-eyed.

'You've lost weight,' he said eventually.

'Yes.' She wanted to scream, to cry, to run into his arms, but she still didn't know why he was here.

Her eyes widened questioningly. 'Why are you here, Max?'

'Rupert came to see me,' he said.

She shook her head in vehement denial. 'Well, he shouldn't have done. He had no right.'

'No.' The word was a flat contradiction. 'I had no right. No right at all to accuse you of something of which you were innocent.'

She felt that her knees were going to buckle under her, and perhaps he saw the slight sway, for he put his hand out as if to steady her, then withdrew it.

'Will you sit down, Shauna? I have something that I want to tell you.'

She complied automatically, her body sinking gratefully into the bursting leather armchair. Grey eyes clashed with green. She felt herself instinctively softening under his gaze, and her lashes quickly dropped to conceal her eyes. She didn't want him to know how vulnerable she was around him. Not now it was all over.

'I never told you very much about my wife,' he began, in the tone of someone who wanted to get the story over with. 'But you guessed that it was not a happy marriage, didn't you?'

She nodded. There had been a cool distance in his voice whenever he had spoken of Blanche, like a man describing a stranger—not a much-loved spouse. She found herself imprisoned in the bright green gaze of his eyes.

'When I met Blanche, we were both very young. She was a very beautiful woman—and I was knocked for six by her.' He ran his hand through already ruffled dark hair. 'I guess we mistook lust for love,' he said at last.

There was a short, intense silence. Shauna could scarcely breathe. Where on earth was all this leading? But she said nothing, just sat and waited.

'She became pregnant.' The voice was harsh. 'And, for the sake of the baby—we married. It was a mistake.' He met her eyes then, staring at her with a candour which triggered off a feeling of hope.

'I'm not saying that we didn't try—because we did. But we were both so very young, and basically incompatible and—it was a difficult time. I was working all hours to get the business started, and, consequently, I was hardly ever there. We had a beautiful house, but not much cash.' He hesitated. 'And then Rupert came back.'

'Rupert?' she echoed, confused.

He nodded. 'We'd grown up together, gone to the same school—we were the best of mates. He wanted to see the world, and when he arrived in Australia he liked it so much that he decided to stay. He didn't come back until Bianca was a few weeks old, when he met Blanche for the first time.' The lines around his mouth were carved as if in stone. 'Rupert had plenty of money to throw around—he was a pretty attractive prospect, and,' he shrugged, 'he and Blanche—fell in love. I didn't know a thing about it—didn't even guess—I was too busy starting up the business.' There was a pause. 'The night she died she was leaving me to go to him.'

Suddenly, she understood. Everything. His furious reaction to the newspaper photo. It must have seemed like a particularly warped instance of history repeating itself. 'Oh, Max,' she cried. 'For God's sake—why didn't you tell me about Rupert?' she demanded.

'When? When I was so busy procrastinating about my own feelings about you? Trying to stay away from you, to fight the way I felt about you? What right did I have to tell you who you should or shouldn't see? I had intended to tell you when I got back from the Cotswolds, but then...'

'But then there was supposed evidence linking me to Rupert,' she said slowly. 'Oh, Max—you didn't even give me a chance to explain. I thought that you were glad of a reason to end it.'

'Glad?' His voice was bleak. 'I wasn't thinking straight at all. I was struck by a jealousy so blinding that I just lashed out. I'd never felt that violently about a woman before, not ever. Afterwards, when I'd had time to think about it, I realised that everything I knew about you—everything in your soft and gentle and funny nature—belied what I believed. Only I thought it was too late, by then. I thought that you'd despise me for my lack of faith. Rupert came to see me today. He told me that it was time we buried the past, for Bianca's sake. That we should each stop blaming the other for Blanche, that she was dead now, and nothing could bring her back. He also told me that there was nothing between you, that, yes—he'd tried it on. But that he was sorry he had because when he saw you, how miserable you were and——'

'Yes,' she said, bitterly. 'Poor little Shauna, moping and pining inside on her own.'

'How miserable I was,' he finished quietly.

She looked up, her grey eyes disbelieving. 'And why should you be miserable, Max?'

'Because I love you.'

Bizarrely, the sound of a car hooting outside the flat intruded on her consciousness. She blinked as if she had imagined it.

'I love you,' he said again, very steadily.

This time she was blinking back salt tears which slid down the back of her throat. She had some questions of her own. 'And what about Marta?' she whispered. 'She was staying in the Cotswolds, too, wasn't she? Were you having a final fling with her?' she finished bitterly.

'What?' he breathed incredulously.

'Marta was there, wasn't she? Why else did you run off the following morning, as if you couldn't wait to be away from me, as if you couldn't wait to get back to her?'

'Yes, Marta was there,' he said quietly. 'I had to get away that morning because I realised that I'd fallen in love with you, and that terrified the hell out of me.' He smiled at her. 'You once asked me what had made me so cynical about women—well, I'll tell you. After Blanche had died there was never a shortage of women, but the fact that all my money was tied up in the business with none left to throw around meant that I was never considered husband material.' He gave a dry laugh. 'How all that changed once I started making it. Those same women suddenly found an overwhelming urge to settle down and discovered that all they had ever really wanted was to bake bread and be waiting by the fireside every night.

'But you,' his gaze softened, 'were different. I knew that you didn't give a damn for the money. I knew that you genuinely cared—and not just for me, but for Bianca, too. That night I spent with you I finally admitted to myself what I think I'd known all along—that I didn't want the kind of "no ties, no questions" relationship that I was used to. Not with you. That with you it was serious business.' The voice lowered. 'All or nothing. The real McCoy. But I also owed it to Marta to tell her that I'd finally fallen in love.'

The impulse to throw herself into his arms was as strong as she'd ever known it. But not yet. 'And what about Trudy?' she persisted.

He laughed. 'I went out with Trudy *years* ago. I kept her on as my accountant because, as I told you—she's superb at her job.' He saw her face. 'However,' he amended hastily, 'I have been thinking of moving to a larger firm of accountants for some time. Listen, sweetheart—there's no one but you. Not since the first day you walked into my office, looking so fresh, and young and vibrant—so different from the other women. You have managed to become a part of my every waking moment. My daughter loves you, Mrs Roberts loves you—every damn person you meet loves you. I was being spectacularly dense not to realise that I was among them.' He smiled. 'I wasn't looking for love, Shauna, or expecting it. It just crept up on me. The night I spent with you was the most perfect of my life, but I just needed a bit of space—to think things through. The question is,' and here he held his hand out to her, 'whether you think you could consider sharing your life with a man to whom trust doesn't come very easily?'

There was no contest. No contest at all. The bottom line was that they loved one another, and wasn't love the finest foundation for trust which existed? She caught the hand and smiled into his eyes. 'I would consider it,' she said, very softly. 'Because I love you very much, and you're going to learn that you can trust me whatever happens.'

He cupped her face in his hands to look at her for a long, precious moment before lowering his mouth on to hers to kiss her with a sweetness which took her breath away, so much that, trembling, she broke the kiss to lean weakly against him, her mouth against the strong column of his neck, her warm breath fanning the smooth skin there.

'And let's face it,' he mused, 'if I hadn't been in love with you, I'd have sacked you weeks ago!'

'Why, you——' But the playful punch was deflected, caught and kissed.

'Can we go home soon?' he whispered. 'Because if those flatmates of yours walk in, they may get something of a shock!'

'Why?' she enquired with teasing innocence as he began to kiss her, but then she gave a small whimper of delight mingled with shock as he moved her hand down to touch him and she realised just how badly he wanted her.

'Let's go home to bed,' he growled. 'Before I do something which could ruin my reputation forever.'

She took a deep breath; she still wasn't sure how he was going to take this. 'Before we do, there's something I ought to tell you.'

Shauna rolled over, reaching out automatically for her watch on the bedside table.

Max gave a muffled moan of protest and his hand moved sensuously round her waist and up, to stroke expertly at her breast. She gave a little sigh of pleasure, but, remembering the time, moved her warm body fractionally away from his.

'Come back here,' he murmured, pulling her back firmly into his arms, to rub the hard evidence of his arousal slowly against the high firmness of her bottom.

'Max,' she protested unconvincingly. 'You really ought to be getting up.'

'That's exactly what I had in mind,' he said wickedly, as he began to kiss the sensitive area behind her ear.

'Max!' The hand had moved from her breast and was now tracing light circles over her flat stomach. 'Stop that! I ought to think about giving David his breakfast.'

'Bianca will do that,' he said easily. 'She's off to university tomorrow, and she'll miss her little brother.'

Shauna snuggled luxuriously into his arms. 'We've hardly seen him since she's been home for the holidays.'

'That's because she loves her brother, and she likes to give her parents a break,' he smiled.

'You must be very proud of her, darling,' she whispered, running a forefinger lightly over the broad chest.

He propped himself up on one elbow and looked down at her lovingly. 'I am,' he agreed. 'And I still find it hard to believe that our tearaway schoolgirl should have turned her hand to law—and won a place at Oxford, to boot. But most of it's down to you, sweetheart—you brought such love and stability into this house when you married me. Bianca couldn't help but flourish, and neither could I.'

He smiled at her tenderly and she was reminded of his face a long time ago, in a small flat on a cold winter's day.

Laughter lit her eyes. 'Do you remember the day I told you I was pregnant?'

'Do I? You sent me reeling!'

She grew warm with pleasure under the approbation in his eyes. 'I was scared you'd mind.' It was not the first time she'd said it.

'Mind? *Mind*?' he chuckled. A lazy hand brushed lightly over her breasts. 'Do you think it's time we started making some more?'

'Oh, yes, please,' she said softly.

'Well, then,' he teased her. 'You shouldn't try and stop your husband from doing what comes very naturally. Now,' he drawled, 'just where was I?'

He moved his hand back to her stomach, and in a leisurely way began to trail it slowly downwards until he had reached the tangle of silky hair, and beyond. She gave a sharp gasp of pleasure. His fingers stayed right where they were, but unmoving, and his eyes were twinkling.

'Want me to stop?'

'No—oh,' she shuddered.

'Sure?'

'Yes!'

'Then tell me you love me.'

'Oh, Max,' she breathed. 'I love you very much.'

'That's good,' he said contentedly, and he bent down and began to kiss her.

HARLEQUIN PRESENTS®

We're not keeping it to ourselves!
Secrets...
The exciting collection of intriguing, sensual stories from Harlequin Presents

Trail of Love by Amanda Browning
Harlequin Presents #1742

Kay Napier was a happy, intelligent young woman who had been brought up in a loving home. Then lightning struck. The first bolt came in the disturbingly attractive shape of Ben Radford. The second was a challenge to her very identity. It was unsettling to discover that she wasn't who she thought she was. But nothing as unnerving as finding that Ben wanted her body, but not her love. And to prove that, Ben intended to marry someone else....

Available in May wherever Harlequin books are sold.

HARLEQUIN®
PRESENTS *Plus*

An affair...with her own husband? Laura and Dirk had been separated but, all of a sudden, he was back in her life and pursuing her. Laura couldn't forget that she had been unable to conceive Dirk's child, which meant there could be no long-term future for them—so why was she still tempted to accept his simply *outrageous* proposal!

Nell was wary of men, until she met Ben Rigby and found herself longing for something more. But she was afraid. Her child—her lost child, whom she'd never had the chance to see—shared the same birthday as Ben's adopted son...was Fate being cruel or kind?

Harlequin Presents Plus—where
women's dreams come true!

Coming next month:

An Outrageous Proposal by Miranda Lee
Harlequin Presents Plus #1737

and

Shadow Play by Sally Wentworth
Harlequin Presents Plus #1738

Harlequin Presents Plus
The best has just gotten better!

Available in May wherever Harlequin books are sold.

PPLUS24

HARLEQUIN®

PRESENTS
RELUCTANT BRIDEGROOMS

Two beautiful brides, two unforgettable romances...
two men running for their lives....

My Lady Love, by Paula Marshall, introduces
Charles, Viscount Halstead, who lost his memory
and found himself employed as a stableboy by the
untouchable Nell Tallboys, Countess Malplaquet.
But Nell didn't consider Charles untouchable—
not at all!

Darling Amazon, by Sylvia Andrew, is the story of
a spurious engagement between Julia Marchant
and Hugo, marquess of Rostherne—an engagement
that gets out of hand and just may lead Hugo to
the altar after all!

Enjoy two madcap Regency weddings this May,
wherever Harlequin books are sold.

Harlequin invites you to the most
romantic wedding of the season.

Rope the cowboy of your dreams in
Marry Me, Cowboy!

A collection of 4 brand-new stories,
celebrating weddings, written by:

New York Times bestselling author

JANET DAILEY

and favorite authors

Margaret Way
Anne McAllister
Susan Fox

Be sure not to miss Marry Me, Cowboy!
coming this April

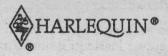 HARLEQUIN®

MMC